# THE BESWICK PRICE GUIDE

## Harvey May

### Fourth Edition

Francis Joseph
London
1997

# Acknowledgements

Thanks are due to my publisher Francis Salmon for once again encouraging me to revise and update all of the information and prices within these covers and to then put it all together for you to enjoy.

Trevor Leak has again been responsible for the cover photograph and many of those contained in the book. I must also thank Laura J Rock-Smith, William L Peck, Stan and Chris Cartledge, Chris and Sue Lane, Edna Holland, Norma Cunningham, Nick Tzimas, Royal Doulton plc and Christie's for additional pictures.

My wife Hazel has been a constant help throughout and her support is so necessary in a project of this kind. Thank you.

I would also like to thank the large numbers of collectors and dealers who are always willing to share information with me and to advise model variations and unusual colourways which they have found.

**Harvey May**

Fourth Edition
Francis Joseph Publishing
All rights reserved. No unauthorised publication or photocopying of information contained in this publication is permitted.

©1997 Harvey May and Francis Joseph Publishing.
Beswick is a registered trademark of Royal Doulton Ltd.

ISBN 1-870703-73-1

Typeset by E J Folkard Print Services
199 Station Road, Crayford, Kent DA1 3QF

Printed by The Greenwich Press
Standard House, Westmoor Street, London SE7.

## Important Notice

To all
Beswick collectors
far and wide

# About the Author

**Harvey May** was born in Wood Green, London in 1932, the son of a Durham miner who had moved to London after the General Strike of 1926. During the war years he was a child evacuee moving from London to the country town of Halstead, Essex. After the interruption of the war years Harvey finished his education at Enfield Technical School and left there to start work in 1949. He married Hazel in 1954 and moved to his present home in Essex in 1958. He has two sons, both married, and three grandsons, who each have their own growing collection.

His first interest in any hobby was the modest but popular schoolboy pastime of collecting bus and train numbers, an interest which took him far and wide on similarly modest transport — his bike!

In 1952 Harvey joined British Railways as Technical Assistant in the Civil Engineer's Office at King's Cross station, but retired from the railway in 1989.

He is currently employed as a Civil Engineering Consultant, on a part time basis, by Railtrack Southern. Throughout this time he has amassed a collection of railway items and many related books.

China and crested ware have always been an area of interest for Harvey and it was the chance purchase of a Beswick Penguin in 1980 which led to a large collection and the quest for information.

The results of his efforts lie between the covers of this book, to be enjoyed by equally enthusiastic collectors.

# Contents

# Introduction

I am very pleased to welcome you to this fourth edition of my Beswick Price Guide. You can have very little idea how rewarding it is to present to you the information contained within these covers. A great deal of hard work is necessary and my wife Hazel and I, try to visit as many antique fairs and Beswick Club meetings as possible, during the course of a year. This way, we meet a large number of both collectors and dealers and have, over the years, made a lot of friends. This has, in turn, led to us being invited to visit other countries and to stay with collectors, in their homes. We have thoroughly enjoyed all of these trips and have, in the process, learnt a lot more about collecting.

It is not always for profit that people become collectors, although it would be silly of me to think that this is not considered. I regularly have people asking me for help and advice, because they have some money to spare and would like to start collecting china, but do not know where to start or what to collect. This introduces fresh blood into the hobby and can only be for the benefit of everyone. We all have knowledge which can be shared and no one should be afraid of helping another collector to start off on the right foot.

Collecting Beswick has now grown to such an extent that one constantly hears the same story that 'there is no Beswick'. I find this hard to believe sometimes and the only conclusion that I can draw is that there are now so many collectors, that most of it must lie in their collections. This leads me to the question of what to collect and what to do when one's shopping list is finished.

To collect what you like is not always possible if you put the 'Duchess with Flowers' down, or some other piece in the high price category. These can always be thoughts for the distant future! Try to have a reason for choosing a certain group, don't just go for, say, birds and then try to get them all. This will not really satisfy you, because as soon as you have done this, you will want to go on to something else. Sometimes it is better to just collect a selection, other times, to select pieces from a range, then again, styles of backstamp may attract you. Always buy what you like, not what you *think* you should buy because someone else has told you to buy it. Try to get pieces that have no damage, as the day will come when you will want to sell and nobody wants to buy damaged pieces. There are exceptions, of course, and a small chip, which is not very obvious, on a rare piece, may well be worth buying, but the price should be adjusted accordingly.

These, then, are just a few thoughts for you, but now we have to be aware of other, more sinister things happening in the collectors world. During the past two to three years, there has been a growing tendency for Beswick ceramic bases to be used, by some people, for mounting models of various animals from other factories. The availability of these bases came about when surplus hollow china bases, of various shapes, 1¼ inches high and with 'Beswick

England' impressed on the them, were sold off in the Beswick factory shop. Animals and figures from other factories, which carry no identification other than a removable sticker, have then been mounted on these bases by unscrupulous persons and then passed off as 'genuine unrecorded pieces from Beswick'.

Needless to say, a premium price tag applies. Another innovation recently has been three mice (1678 in the current range) mounted on one of these bases and with on-glaze 'bandages' painted round the eyes and head, with a name-plate applied reading 'Three Blind Mice'. Although all of the models had been made at Beswick, the combined pieces had not and it was not a factory issue.

The third and potentially hardest 'fraud' is the reproduction backstamp (which is practically perfect) on to a non-Beswick item. These 'copy back-stamps' are hard to detect and will fool most people, unless they are very experienced in recognising Beswick shapes, styles and decoration.

These then are some of the pitfalls which you should be aware of, but I would like to make it absolutely clear that the number of people doing this sort of thing is very, very small and that the vast majority of dealers would have nothing to do with it. Nevertheless, you should be aware that it is taking place and be on the lookout.

Incidentally, in 15 years of collecting Beswick, I have yet to find anything which is unrecorded and marked Beswick. So, having said all this, the good news is that new models are still coming out, carrying the Beswick backstamp, but most of them are special commissions. In themselves they are very good models of the animals and characters which they portray and the limited numbers which are available (up to 2000) ensures that there are enough to go round for everybody. There is, of course, a penalty to pay in that the price is higher than for other, similar, models, which are released by Royal Doulton through retail outlets. I am afraid that this seems to be the only way, at present, of having something made to order and exclusive. There has been a very good response from collectors to these special editions and I think that if 'the subject' matter is right and not too many produced, then we can all look forward to seeing a few more. Don't forget that it is Royal Doulton who set the minimum edition number and hence, the price and the person making the commission has then to judge whether the price is going to be acceptable to you, the collector. The other type of commission is the one which is only available at one special fair and on one day only, by those attending the fair. This was very successful at the Dunstable Doulton and Beswick Fair, on Sunday 19th October, 1996 when most of the 1250 sets of Meerkats was sold. On this occasion the commissioned number was lower and the price was good value at £35 per pair. I know that collectors, unable to attend, were keen to get a set and this was catered for by putting aside a small number and advertising them in *Collecting Doulton* magazine. The edition is now closed.

The newest and perhaps one of the most popular, is the special limited edition of 1997 pieces, featuring Mrs Rabbit and the Four Bunnies on a china base, which itself stands on a wooden plinth carrying an engraved name plate. It has a special Beswick backstamp and a certificate of authenticity and is issued to commemorate the fiftieth anniversary of the first production of

Beatrix Potter figures at the Beswick factory. This is a prestigious piece featuring Mrs Rabbit and her four children, Flopsy, Mopsy, Cottontail and Peter Rabbit and is issued by the John Beswick Studios. I think that the demand for this very special piece will far outstrip the number available and it will become a very desirable model to have.

All of this has given a boost to collectors and a general feeling that the backstamp is here to stay, at least for the foreseeable future. It surely must be easier to build on the past success of a trade mark than to diminish its availability and replace it with another.

1993 saw the first ever large size Beatrix Potter model and the one chosen was Peter Rabbit. There have subsequently been nine further characters, modelled to the same large size, but only one other carries the Beswick mark.

The real surprise introduction and a 'first' for Beswick, was the set of six busts, based upon characters from the TV series *Thunderbirds* and only available by post in a numbered edition. Other new introductions, within two years, amounted to some 80 models and this formidable list includes the nine superb *Pig's Prom*, the eight very detailed *Country Friends*, three Badgers, a Harvest Mouse and a Wood Mouse, ten small size Dogs and several farm animals from the current range, now available on bases. The 16 remaining original medium size dogs have now been withdrawn.

To mark Beswick's Centenary in 1994, the special size 'Jemima Puddleduck' figure was accompanied by 'Cancara', the black horse, both carrying the Beswick stamp for 1994 only. These models herald a new era in the development of the Beswick brand and were most welcome additions to the range.

Overall, I think Beswick collectors have been given a great deal of consideration, and it is to be hoped that Royal Doulton will have one or two more surprises in store. This may be a good time to state, quite categorically, that the John Beswick factory is still very much in business and has a very full production schedule. All 92 Beswick-marked models still in production are made and decorated here, along with a wide range of Royal Doulton marked character jugs and figures and, of course, all of the Beatrix Potter models, marked Royal Albert, are made here also.

It is surprising how many people believe that the Beswick factory is closed. In fact, there is a fine museum with a good representative collection of many of the older decorative wares and figures, together with a showroom containing current production pieces. Factory tours are available, Monday-Friday, both morning and afternoon, and are thoroughly recommended. The tour takes about 1¼ hours and finishes in the factory shop, where there is a good range of products for sale, frequently at advantageous prices.

The factory is in Gold Street, Longton, Stoke-on-Trent and tours can be arranged through Joan Barker, telephone 01782 291213 or Royal Doulton on 01782 292292. The Gladstone Pottery Museum is nearby and the two can be conveniently visited in one day.

Since my last book was published, Beswick models have continued to increase in popularity and some of the well liked items are now very hard to find. Even the more common pieces are sometimes quite difficult to find and, of course, the rarer models command a much higher price.

Details of all models which have been allocated a shape number in the Beswick pattern book are again listed under the different headings and are up-to-date with regard to new introductions and withdrawals.

THROUGHOUT THE BOOK, A MODEL WHICH IS STILL MADE TODAY AT THE BESWICK FACTORY IS MARKED 'C' IN THE LISTS. THE PRICE QUOTED IS THE CURRENT SUGGESTED RETAIL SELLING PRICE, INCLUDING 17½% VAT, AS GIVEN IN THE JANUARY 1997 PRICE LIST PUBLISHED BY ROYAL DOULTON.

Top favourites still seem to be the Beatrix Potter models, although the several Walt Disney and David hand series are very much in demand.

Marilyn Sweet's *Guide to Horses, Ponies & Foals* published in 1992, filled the gap very nicely and was well received by all collectors of horses.

All models in the following groups, and which originally carried the Beswick mark, are now in the Royal Doulton series and a new DA (Doulton Animals) number has been allocated:

1) Connoisseur
2) Horses
3) Foals
4) 'Fireside' Dogs and Cat
5) Old English Dogs (1378/3 to 1378/7)
6) Dogs (medium) 3055 and above
7) Spirit Dogs on plinth (matt)
8) 'Good Companion' Dogs (2982 and above)
9) Cats

All now carry the Royal Doulton backstamp, and all are still made in the Beswick factory. Full details of the new DA and old Beswick numbers are given and will help identification.

Now that the initial upset amongst collectors over the use of the Royal Albert mark on Beatrix Potter figures has died down, it is time to see what effect it has had.

First of all, there has been a very long 'offer' period on the standard price figures, with 1993 seeing the price at £9.95 and the 1994 and 1995 price being £10.95 whilst in 1996 it was £11.95. All years saw these prices held for varying periods and sales should have been quite healthy. December 1995 saw the withdrawal of six figures, of which one (3251) 'Miss Dormouse', had only been produced for four years and was I thought, quite a nice model. Another (3157), 'Peter in the Gooseberry Net' had only been produced for five years and both had only ever carried the Royal Albert mark. 'Old Mr Bouncer' (2956) was also taken out of production and is of interest in that it carried the Albert mark for longer than the Beswick.

This might be the right place to say that in recording the modelling activities of the John Beswick factory today, I have to stray over the purely 'Beswick' line now and again, but it is done so that you can have as complete a picture as possible of what is going on.

December 1996 saw the withdrawal of six more figures, three which carried both the Beswick and Albert mark (2878, 2957 & 2996) and three which only carried the Albert mark (2966, 3200 and 3288). Advance notice has been given that more are to be withdrawn at the end of 1997.

So we now have a situation where Royal Doulton themselves are creating a collectors' market by the early withdrawal of figures from a very popular range. New model variations continue to turn up and this adds a bit of spice for the observant collector. No records were kept of these changes as they were mostly made to ease production problems.

The 'Beswick Bears' group suddenly appeared at a handful of outlets and without any publicity at all towards the end of 1993. They were resin models of bears, about 3" high and all doing something different and enjoying a picnic party. Superbly detailed and carrying a *Beswick Bears* label on the base, each piece was named and carried a suitable verse (e.g. 'Sam' plays his banjo all day long, amusing friends with a tune and a song). Standard green Beswick boxes were used for packaging, with *Beswick Bears* printed on the side.

Very limited marketing appears to have taken place and the whole series is now very collectable. The comment that 'collectors are not aware of new products' certainly seems to be true in the case of the Bears.

Another group appeared in October 1994, again of resin and very similar to the Bears. The series was named *Country Cousins* and portrayed several different small animals. They are numbered PM2101 to PM2120 but only 17 models were produced. They are marketed with a brand name of 'Beswick International' and made in (the country of) China.

Some of the 'Little Loveable' series of clown models have become hard to find and are now quite collectable. These include the matt finish models, the plain ones with no logo and the last two in the series. In addition, 'God Loves Me' in all three varieties is desirable.

Once again, the awareness of collecting Beswick in Australia, New Zealand, North America and Canada has increased, but unfortunately, in South Africa there are not the same opportunities and the number of collectors has shown no increase at all.

Closure of the Beswick Collectors Circle, after 10 years, was a blow, but formation of the Beswick Collectors Club, though *Collecting Doulton* magazine, has helped to hold things together. If you wish to attend meetings, around the country, where you meet, sell & buy and have the opportunity of ordering models specially commissioned from Beswick, then you should take out a subscription for the magazine and and make it absolutely clear that you are interested in the Beswick club. Only then will you be advised of events, which are strictly for members only.

Many new collectors of Beswick have already been interested in Doulton for a number of years and are merely broadening their horizons, but there are also a very sizeable number of new collectors who have been attracted to Beswick.

All of this activity points to a healthy collecting market and it is hoped that new models will continue to attract the attention of collectors. Values have continued to rise in some collecting areas and there have been some pretty spectacular prices paid at some of the specialist auctions. There have also been some price reductions, as collecting habits have changed and ideas modified. There are now four major UK collectors fairs which feature Beswick alongside the well-established Doulton wares. These are held at Trentham gardens, Stoke-on-Trent, in early June, at Dunstable in October, and the newest fair, organised by the Doulton and Beswick Dealers Association, is held at the Birmingham Motor Cycle Museum in March and August.

A frequent request since Beswick became so popular was for more pictures and this was met, during 1994, with the publication by UK International Ceramics of a special numbered limited edition of 1,000 copies of a 1959 Beswick catalogue. With over 600 illustrations, it nicely fills the pictorial gap for collectors. This was followed in 1996 by a further catalogue of Beswick Products from 1950-1996 & the two together form a handy pictorial reference for collectors.

Some items which have been listed in the three previous Beswick collectors books have been taken out of this edition and will appear in the more suitable *Decorative Wares Handbook* which is still in the course of preparation.

This leads me to remind you that all prices quoted are only a guide as to what you might expect to pay. They are not auction results but average Fair prices and you must **always** make your **own** decision on what you actually pay, depending on condition.

*Colin Melbourne **1481** Reindeer and **1465** Zebra – two of the eight wild animal models in this series.*

12

# Collecting Beswick

My interest developed from collecting crested china wares which are, on the whole, not very colourful. Visiting antique fairs is an enjoyable way of not only looking for something which is pleasing to the eye, but also where you can meet people and, quite often, make friends. Everyone acquires knowledge about their hobby and it is only by sharing information that we all learn more.

It was in the early 1980s that, whilst visiting a Fair, a penguin with an orange umbrella over its head caught my eye. The modelling and touch of humour appealed to me and my first purchase of Beswick took place at the modest price of £2!

The seeds of collecting were sown and I was hooked!

Gradually I built up a small collection of pieces and regularly attended Fairs simply to look for more Beswick. Questions arose — 'How many are there in the set?' 'Who modelled this or that piece?' 'When was it made?'

There were few answers forthcoming from dealers, who only put Beswick on their shelves because of its obvious quality.

So began my quest for more knowledge and also research to find some answers to the many questions which I had, not least of which was 'Who are Beswick?', 'When did they start?', 'What makes them produce the things they do?'

The more I researched through old catalogues the more I became aware of the great diversity and range of Beswick, from colourful Christmas tankards to the spectacular lifelike models of wild animals, such as the African Elephant. The company has consistently produced excellent models of horses, dogs and wild animals, and is well established as a specialist in its field.

Many of the Beswick models are superb and I think that the Connoisseur Collection, in particular, represents the very best in artistic design and detail. The subjects cover award-winning show dogs, famous racehorses, wild animals and birds, all on a mahogany plinth and ready to take pride of place on any collector's shelf.

Beswick models are not only accurate and detailed but are appealing to! Humour is very much to the fore, as in the cat playing the violin or the happy mongrel dog with outrageously proportioned limbs and head. Even models not specifically intended to be funny are often engaging in their poses, and this certainly adds to the enjoyment of collecting.

The Company has certainly stood the test of time and the basis of this success can be attributed mainly to the work of John Ewart and Gilbert Beswick who broke new ground in the thirties.

Art Director James Hayward also deserves special mention here because he had over thirty designers working under him during the period 1934 to 1969 when Royal Doulton took over the company and he continued to work for Beswick until his retirement in 1975.

The number of people who are Beswick collectors is very considerable and, through them, I am able to keep 'tabs' on most of the model variations which turn up.

My initial research into Beswick history and product information was hampered by the very limited amount available and so I contacted the factory for help. Very little was available and I was invited to examine the old pottery books. From these and other sources I have been able to trace the production details of Beswick's output since the 1930s.

With more knowledge gained I have updated all of the lists with the latest available information on variations, colours and prices and I hope that you will be able to 'pin down' those unusual finds. Additionally, I have noted models finished in a matt deco, together with their production run.

Once again, I hope that you will enjoy this book which, if not your introduction to the world of Beswick, will at least update your knowledge a little.

## Collecting tips and valuing discontinued Beswick

Once collectors become 'hooked' they often find it difficult to know when to stop buying and this can create all kinds of problems, particularly if the pieces are very expensive. Beswick wares are now very collectable and some prices have risen steeply during the last two years. No longer is it possible to find relatively rare models at bargain prices. The number of possible collecting subjects is enormous though and the best way of starting is by choosing a specific theme such as 'Horses', 'Beatrix Potters' or 'humourous subjects'.

This book gives details of the variety available, but it is a good idea to find out what the current price range is for the chosen pieces before embarking on

*The 'Bedtime Chorus' in full voice. L–R, shape numbers **1826/01/02/03/04/24/05/25**. A very delicate set.*

an area which is too expensive. It is no good deciding to collect a particular series without knowing how many pieces there are and how much you are likely to have to spend to make a complete collection.

The only guide as to the value or worth of a particular piece is the amount that the collector is prepared to spend. As the market for Beswick continues to develop, collectors will become more and more aware of which models are the hardest to find and, in accordance with the dictates of supply and demand, the prices of these are bound to rise more than the rest. This is what makes collecting so enjoyable, particularly the pleasure of a 'find' which is picked up at a reasonable price.

The collector will find this book useful for identifying models, their dates of production and withdrawal, but it must be noted that some of the pieces do not have the model number impressed on their base and that where the base is too small for the Beswick mark it may only have the 'England' stamp on it. In these cases the collector, coming across the model for the first time at an antiques fair, may not recognise it as Beswick.

PLEASE NOTE THAT MODELS PREVIOUSLY AVAILABLE WITH A BESWICK BACKSTAMP, BUT NOW CURRENTLY AVAILABLE WITH EITHER A ROYAL DOULTON OR ROYAL ALBERT MARK, COMMAND A HIGHER PRICE AS DISCONTINUED BESWICK. There is an unconfirmed rumour that the Beswick mark is to be more widely used in 1998.

The difficulties involved in finding the final additions to a collection add to the pleasure of 'the hunt', which is, after all, what it is all about. GOOD HUNTING!

*Mr Alderman Ptolemy* **2424**; *left and Sir Isaac Newton* **2425**, *were the first Beatrix Potter production models never to carry a Gold Backstamp.*

# Model Numbers

So far as is known every item produced since 1933 has been allocated a model number.

In some cases, for example wall mounted plaques of birds in flight, sets of different size models will be given the same number.

Colour variations also occur among animals, Dickens ware and B.P. figures, with the same number applying each time. Many of the animals are available in either gloss or matt finish and some can be found with or without a china or wooden base. In all cases the same model number applies.

Most of the pre-war bird, wild and farm animal models were decorated in several different colours. The more unusual shades command a higher price. A popular colour was blue – usually marked 8700 – and this was used on many early models and in all groups up to 1940.

Dates of withdrawal are given with information taken from annual price lists.

The following table gives the design date for each model:

| Model Numbers | | | Design Date | Model Numbers | | | Design Date |
|---|---|---|---|---|---|---|---|
| 1 | — | 377 | Undated | 1921 | — | 1996 | 1964 |
| 378 | — | 460 | 1936 | 1997 | — | 2053 | 1965 |
| 461 | — | 567 | 1937 | 2054 | — | 2086 | 1966 |
| 568 | — | 672 | 1938 | 2087 | — | 2176 | 1967 |
| 673 | — | 794 | 1939 | 2177 | — | 2255 | 1968 |
| 795 | — | 880 | 1940 | 2256 | — | 2302 | 1969 |
| 881 | — | 968 | 1941 | 2303 | — | 2349 | 1970 |
| 969 | — | 990 | 1942 | 2350 | — | 2396 | 1971 |
| 991 | — | 1000 | 1943 | 2397 | — | 2443 | 1972 |
| 1001 | — | 1013 | 1944 | 2444 | — | 2500 | 1973 |
| 1014 | — | 1042 | 1945 | 2501 | — | 2522 | 1974 |
| 1043 | — | 1082 | 1946 | 2523 | — | 2554 | 1975 |
| 1083 | — | 1107 | 1947 | 2555 | — | 2582 | 1976 |
| 1108 | — | 1141 | 1948 | 2583 | — | 2607 | 1977 |
| 1142 | — | 1180 | 1949 | 2608 | — | 2636 | 1978 |
| 1181 | — | 1209 | 1950 | 2637 | — | 2666 | 1979 |
| 1210 | — | 1226 | 1951 | 2667 | — | 2700 | 1980 |
| 1227 | — | 1279 | 1952 | 2701 | — | 2750 | 1981 |
| 1280 | — | 1322 | 1953 | 2751 | — | 2804 | 1982 |
| 1323 | — | 1362 | 1954 | 2805 | — | 2846 | 1983 |
| 1363 | — | 1391 | 1955 | 2847 | — | 2899 | 1984 |
| 1392 | — | 1468 | 1956 | 2900 | — | 2960 | 1985 |
| 1469 | — | 1516 | 1957 | 2961 | — | 3031 | 1986 |
| 1517 | — | 1576 | 1958 | 3032 | — | 3114 | 1987 |
| 1577 | — | 1667 | 1959 | 3115 | — | 3179 | 1988 |
| 1668 | — | 1732 | 1960 | 3180 | — | 3225 | 1989 |
| 1733 | — | 1792 | 1961 | 3226 | — | 3275 | 1990 |
| 1793 | — | 1861 | 1962 | 3276 | — | 3330 | 1991 |
| 1862 | — | 1920 | 1963 | 3331 | — | | 1992 |

# A Century of Progress!

How proud James Wright Beswick would have been to know that the family potting business, started in 1894, would be celebrating its centenary this year and still producing high quality products under the umbrella of Royal Doulton (UK) Limited.

The Beswicks were originally from Bolton, in Lancashire – the cotton county – and during the 1830s they moved to the parish of Chell, in Staffordshire, where they soon developed coal interests.

In 1840, Robert Beswick, in partnership with John Leese, bought a piece of land in Tunstall and built a small 'pot bank'. There were already hundreds of similar small factories producing earthenware and rough-cast figures and competition must have been fierce. The factory was named 'Churchbank' and manufacture of earthenwares commenced straight away and continued until 1857 when it was leased out, with a condition that 'all coal for potting should be supplied from Beswick-owned mines'. No significant change took place until 1891 when 'Churchbank' was sold to Thomas Booth, who developed 'good quality earthenware shapes, delicately potted and light in weight'.

Meanwhile, the coal mine was being run by Robert Beswick's two sons, Robert and James Wright, and it was the latter who, in 1894, went into business on his own and established a potting trade in Longton, one of the six towns which make up the Staffordshire Potteries.

He took a five-year lease on the Baltimore Works in Albion Street and production of an increasing variety of plain and decorated ware commenced.

Two years later, the lease of a second factory – the Britannia Works in Longton High Street – was taken and then again, in 1898, a third lease, this time to the present home of Beswick, the Gold Street Works.

Expansion here was fast and additional kilns were quickly built and contributed to a 'very modern and completely fitted-up factory'.

The following year – 1899 – saw the Baltimore Works lease run out and all china production appears to have been concentrated at the Brittania Works. Everything points to the production of china having been ceased here when the lease ran out in 1905.

Meanwhile, expansion at Gold Street continued and James Wright's eldest son, John, who had been involved in the business for a number of years, was made a partner with a salary of £4 per week and he immediately took control of manufacturing.

According to a report in the March 1906 *Pottery Gazette* '. . . almost everything in earthenware is made here . . .' and special mention is made of chimney ornaments.

It is of interest here to say that Royal Doulton currently produce five Traditional Staffordshire Dog models still using the original Beswick moulds.

In 1908, the works of Bridgett & Bates in King Street, Longton were acquired, so that china production could re-establish once again.

Production of china marked 'Aldwych China' continued here until 1914 when the factory was closed down, sold and production transferred to the more modern Warwick Works in Chadwick Street, Longton. The factory was probably leased until being taken over in 1918 and all china produced here, from that time, was backstamped 'Beswick & Sons'.

Earthenware production continued at the Gold Street Works, whilst all china was made at Chadwick Street until this factory closed in the early 1930s.

The company had now enjoyed 20 years of uninterrupted expansion and had survived the Great War. Their products were aimed at the popular market and prices were consistently below those of their rivals. New introductions kept the interests of retailers and consumers and there was a constant improvement in quality. Trade was brisk and Beswick began exporting to the Dominions.

By 1919, consumers were again buying the things which had been denied them during the war and the trade boom quickly helped to re-establish the pottery trade once again.

In May, 1920 at the age of 75, James Wright Beswick died and the firm was taken over by his son, John. James Wright Beswick had never been properly trained as a potter and he had learnt by trial and error and common sense. His son, John, had the advantage of some technical training and had also attended classes at the Pottery School in Tunstall.

James Wright Beswick was a JP, a member of the old Longton Council, member of Kidsgrove on the first Staffordshire County Council and, later, a Councillor for the City of Stoke-on-Trent. He was also a prominent leader in the Methodist Church affairs and chairman of the old Longton School Board.

The potting trade now suffered the effects of the depression and there was very limited opportunity to make any significant improvement. John Beswick was now the Managing Director at the age of 51 and he was to steer the company through the twenties and into the thirties with a careful policy of improving quality and concentrating more on ornamental ware production.

Beswick products at this time consisted of toiletware, gilt and enamelled jugs and vases, decorated dishes and fruit bowls, together with many other decorative shapes. China and tea ware from the Warwick Works was of fine quality and used the decorative technique of tint-on-print (colouring in parts of transfer prints) on many items. Gilding was still carried out and did not stop until the mid-sixties.

The Beswick family tree is complex and Gilbert (John's stepbrother) went to work at Beswick, after leaving High School in about 1922, and seems to have spent much of his time in the decorating shop. This was to have far-reaching effects later on and was also a contributing factor in Beswick's success story.

In 1926 two men, who were to become central figures in the team, joined the company – Jim Hayward, the future Art Director and Albert Hallam, who was to become acknowledged as the most talented mould-maker in the Potteries.

Like most people living in the Potteries, Jim Hayward came from a family which, for many generations, had been involved in the pottery industry at

Coalport in Coalbrookdale. His career began at the Royal Art Factory, Longton where he was apprenticed to his father. At 16 he left as a protest against working with lead paint without protection and joined Beswick as a painter improver. He was appointed Assistant Manager to Mr Dean, the Decorating Manager, and when Mr Dean departed in 1934 he became Decorating Manager.

Albert Hallam joined Beswick in 1926 at the age of fourteen as an apprentice mould-maker. His father, also called Albert, was already a Beswick clay manager and it was not long before young Albert became a 'block and caser' and eventually head of the mould-making department. Following further training, he became a modeller and was better able to understand the problems of making moulds.

By 1933, Jim Hayward, together with Mr. Dean, had perfected a range of new matt glazes with which they decorated a variety of ornamental ware, all colour being applied with a spray. A piece of sponge was used if a stippled effected was wanted.

Ultimately, more than 50 girls were employed to meet the demand and the Beswick 'Matt Glaze Girls' became famous throughout the potteries.

John Beswick died in 1934 and his son John Ewart became Chairman and Managing Director.

There was now a team in place which was to remain together until the mid-1970s. The only addition would be in 1939 when Arthur Gredington joined the company as its first resident sculptor. Up until this time, much work had been by freelance modellers and certainly nothing like Arthur Gredington's very first model had been seen before at Beswick.

Racehorse 'Bois Russel' won the 1939 Derby and was entered in the Beswick pattern book in March 1939 as model no 701. It was the first realistically modelled horse by Beswick and the forerunner of more than 70 different horse models by Arthur Gredington, up until his final one in 1968.

Gilbert Beswick was now the Sales Director and his 'shop-floor' knowledge was to prove invaluable in being able to accept orders, often with tight delivery times, and to assess likely production problems which might arise. He was a kindly man, a lifelong member of the local Bourne Methodist Church, loved and respected by both employees and customers, but unfortunately the best interests of the Company were not always given priority.

He would agree to very small orders from agents, specially decorated horses and dogs for customers (with detail taken from photographs) and for special items to be modelled, with limited appeal to the market as a whole.

Many of these orders made little or no profit for the factory and caused friction with Ewart Beswick. This led to disagreements, which affected everyone and he would not admit to having made wrong decisions. Later, he would realise his mistakes and apologise and express regret for the upset caused.

Despite this, he was greatly concerned with employee's family troubles and welfare and gave much practical help and kindness, when necessary. Many of the factory workers were members of the Bourne Church and many followed their parents in obtaining employment at Beswicks.

When children reached the age of 14 and had attended Chapel and Sunday

School regularly and whose parents were already employed at Beswicks, then Gilbert would say to them 'when you leave school, you come and see me'. When the time came, the child would speak to Gilbert and be told to 'come along to Beswick on Monday at 7am.' Being the youngest meant doing all sorts of jobs and stoking up the fires was one which was important, so that at 9.30am, when there was a breakfast break, you could have a hot drink and cook bacon and egg, if you had taken it with you. The next job was brushing up all the fires and generally tidying up. There were no canteen facilities, unlike today, and you had to stand in a queue to make tea. If you had a meat pie with for dinner, this could be heated on the fire, together with potatoes and vegetables, which would be cooked in a chamber pot.

Other odd jobs would be carried out around the factory and gradually the child would see the different processes being carried out. Everyone would go home at 5.30pm except the two youngest employees and they would stay until 6pm and do all the sweeping up, before taking the post to the post box.

Saturday mornings were worked from 7am to 12.30pm and one week's paid holiday was given. If you did not go away, you could work as usual.

Youngsters often started learning on the white (undecorated) ware and collected finished pieces for packing. Then, when extra help was needed, they were given some of the less coloured ware to decorate; chambers, ewers, posy bowls and jugs, but not dinner plates.

When Gilbert thought that you knew what you were doing, he would allow you to try something else. He would be all over the factory, every day, and he would himself start at 8am and would first of all check that all staff were in.

Quality was the first priority and if work was not up to standard, then

*Ewart Beswick*                    *Gilbert Beswick*

Gilbert would soon tell the person responsible. Jim Hayward, Decorating Manager, would often stand at the door of the decorating shop and watch the girls decorating the ware and if they did not do it right, he would show them the correct way.

The number of employees at Beswick in the late 1930s was around 100 and fifty years later this had risen to around 500. There are currently approximately 380 employed at Beswick.

In 1938 the business became a private limited company (John Beswick Ltd) and was converted to a public company in 1957.

Decorators usually stayed on the same type of work, some did cottage ware and others salad ware and there was no painting on tea ware. One person would usually stick to the same pattern and this explains why there is frequently very little to choose between several of the earlier decorative pieces when some of the same pattern are compared.

Tube lining and gilding were all carried out by one person until work of this nature ceased in the mid-1960s. All decorating colours were individual and had to be mixed up as required. Aerographers were each given half a pint of milk daily and this was usually boiled up and used as a hot drink. The rate of pay for a girl decorator, at the age of 21, was £1.15 per 5½ day week. Aerographing uses a quick drying water-based paint which is sprayed on and dries as a powder. Using a clean dry brush, any desired decorative effect can be obtained by brushing off some of the paint. This process is used on both vases and animal figures.

Firing of the ware meant that the man in charge of the bottle oven was responsible for the most critical part of the whole process of pottery production. He was the highest paid employee and was in charge of the whole output from the factory covering several days. Bad firing could result in severe losses and he would have to stay up with each oven, for probably 60 hours or more, to ensure that all was well. Ventilation had to be adjusted and temperature maintained and probably 10 tonnes of coal would have to be shovelled – by hand. Is it any wonder that vast quantities of ale were consumed!

When the wares in the bottle oven were ready and it was judged possible to enter, the men went in wearing only a cap and an old sack or piece of cloth tied around their middle and frequently no shoes! Sweat would pour off them as they climbed inside and right up to the top to get the wares out. This was generally about 16 feet up and wooden ladders called 'osses' were used. The wares were in clay containers called 'saggars' and they each weighed about 40-50lbs. An oven might contain up to 2,000 saggars.

When the oven had been cleared each man would be paid 12½p 'beer money' and his services would no longer be required.

The ovens were drawn once a week and every other week a smaller oven was drawn. On these days there would be a queue outside Beswick and if there were insufficient regular workers, then the wares man would go down and make a selection. If you were a good worker, then you would be asked to come again. There was no need to employ the men full time.

During the 1939-45 war a large amount of plain white earthenware was supplied to the RAF but all other items continued in production on a much-

*Arthur Gredington, modeller from 1939 to 1968.*

*Albert Hallam, mould maker and modeller from 1926-75.*

reduced scale. Beswick had bought the adjoining China Bank of H. M. Williamson (trading as Heathcote China) in 1941 and it is here that the RAF earthenware was made.

With the ending of the war, there was no sudden return to normality. Shortages of raw materials, transport difficulties and Government restrictions on both production and decorated ware meant that much development was stifled.

The early 1950s saw the same management team at the helm and plans for expansion were made. In 1957 the adjoining firm of Thomas Lawrence (trading as Falcon Ware) was bought and considerable alterations and rebuilding took place and a lot of the old Beswick buildings were knocked down. It is believed that the bottle ovens were demolished when rebuilding took place and these were replaced by modern gas-fired tunnel ovens where the gradually rising and strictly controlled temperatures reaches a maximum of 1170°C.

In 1961 Harry Sales left E. Brain & Co. and started work at Beswick as a Modelling Assistant to Jim Hayward, the Art Director. When Jim Hayward retired in 1975, Harry Sales was appointed Design Manager, a position he held until 1986.

Graham Tongue joined Beswick in April 1966 and became head modeller when Albert Hallam retired in 1973. When Harry Sales left in 1986 Graham took over responsibility for both design and modelling and continued until 1996. Two other modellers worked for Beswick, David Lyttleton from 1973-86 and Alan Maslankowski from 1973-76. Both still model occasionally for Beswick.

By the late 1960s Ewart Beswick was ready to retire and had no son or heir to whom he could pass control of his business. The Company's reputation was such that it was bought by Royal Doulton, as part of its own development plants, in 1969.

At this time, in addition to the animal, bird and figure ranges, there were still over 100 different ornamental items in production, together with modern designs in the 'Kashan' vase range and 'Zorba' and 'Orbit' tableware.

By the end of 1973 all tableware and vase production had ceased and there was naturally an increasing Royal Doulton influence on design.

The Bunnikins series commenced in 1972 and the design and production has continued there ever since, alongside Brambly Hedge, Winnie the Pooh and Beatrix Potter figures.

The Beswick factory is a friendly place in which to work and with a varying range of figures, character jugs, horses, birds and animals being produced, the future looks secure.

The popular 'Beswick England' backstamp is still used on many of the products coming from the factory and these stand proudly alongside others carrying the Royal Doulton or Royal Albert mark.

Marketing of the John Beswick brand name has been enhanced by the introduction of the 'Little Loveable' clown models, the 'English Country Folk Figures', the limited edition set of six 'Thunderbird' characters, the large size models of Beartrix Potter & The Pig Prom.

These fine new additions are a tribute to Beswick's continuing expertise in this area of ceramics.

*The Gold Street Works circa 1900.*

# Part One: Animals

The name of Beswick is synonymous with meticulously faithful models of animals. The appointment of Arthur Gredington as modeller in 1939 was a major factor in the success of Beswick, for his original models were outstanding. When his skill was combined with that of mouldmaker, Arthur Hallam, and the patient attention and detail of the Beswick paintresses, the quality of the finished Beswick animal was assured.

## Birds

(All current birds carry a Beswick backstamp)
Many varieties and styles of birds are to be found in the Beswick collection. The earliest models were of a ornamental nature, but they soon became more realistic. Later on in the 1930s it became fashionable to model birds in the form of wall plaques and today these are a very collectable series. Mr Watkin was the chief exponent of these particular ornaments and he followed his success with ducks by introducing sets of seagulls, pheasants and blue-tits in flight.

In contrast to the birds on the wing, Beswick artists also modelled a number of species of birds perched on boughs and tree trunks adorned with flowers and these were particularly popular in the late thirties. Until around 1965 the petals and leaves on the bases were modelled in high relief, but as these were vulnerable to damage they were subsequently replaced with hand-painted flowers in low relief.

During the 1950s Colin Melbourne modelled some birds in the modern style, and these were known and marked as the 'C.M.' series and numbered in the '1400' range. He was also responsible for the collection of decoy ducks (1518-1529) which were modelled from the birds sheltering in Peter Scott's sanctuary at Slimbridge. Jim Hayward was the Art Director at the time and he visited Peter Scott to select the species to be portrayed. The first model in this set of twelve was produced in four sizes (see listing), the next two in three sizes and the remaining birds were made in one size only. These models are very collectable, and hard to find.

In recent years Graham Tongue has tended to work on the bird collection. To ensure that his models are accurate, he visits local aviaries and also the Natural History department of the City Museum and Art Gallery, Stoke-on-Trent, and the results of his research are evident in his studies for the Connoisseur range, the Golden Eagle (2062) and the Pheasant (2760). Since 1983 models have been available in either glossy or matt finish, with the exception of the Pheasant (2760).

More recently he has sculpted some superb pieces, but these all now carry the Royal Doulton backstamp and therefore are not be listed here.

Two of the small size birds, introduced in 1991, were modelled by Martyn Alcock, who joined Beswick in 1986 on a Youth Training Scheme. He has since modelled a wide variety of pieces, under Graham's watchful eye.

With regard to the eight small birds, each in two versions, the best way to tell the difference is to look for the impressed number and 'B' backstamp on the base. These only appy to the first versions the re-modelled ones just have the 'Beswick England' stamp.

| Model No | Name of Model | Size inches | Current Value £ | US$ | Production Period |
|---|---|---|---|---|---|
| 450/1 | Penguin | 8 | 100-125 | 200-250 | 1936-1940 |
| 450/2 | Penguin | 3½ | 45-50 | 90-100 | 1936-1955 |
| 617 | Duck | 3 | 45-50 | 90-100 | 1938-1955 |
| 618 | Puffin | — | 80-100 | 160-200 | 1938-1955 |
| 749 | Mallard (rising) | 6½ | 85-100 | 180-200 | 1939-1965 |
| 750 | Mallard (settling) | 6½ | 85-100 | 180-200 | 1939-1965 |
| 754 | Pheasant ash tray | 3½ | 10-15 | 20-30 | 1939-1971 |
| 755 | Duck ash tray | 4 | 10-15 | 20-30 | 1939-1969 |
| 756/1 | Mallard | 7 | 40-45 | 80-90 | 1939-1973 |
| 756/2 | Mallard | 5¾ | 30-35 | 60-70 | 1939-1973 |
| 756/2A | Mallard | 4½ | 25-30 | 50-60 | 1939-1973 |
| 756/3 | Mallard | 3½ | 20-25 | 40-50 | 1939-1973 |
| 767 | Pheasant (curved tail) | 3 | 10-15 | 20-30 | 1939-1971 |
| *767 | Pheasant (straight tail) | 3 | 10-15 | 20-30 | 1971-1994 |
| 768 | Arctic Tern | 8½ | 150-200 | 300-400 | 1939-1955 |
| 800 | Penguin (small) | 2 | 10-15 | 20-30 | 1940-1973 |
| 801 | Penguin (small) | 2 | 10-15 | 20-30 | 1940-1973 |
| | Part of set (see 802 & 803 Novelties) | | | | |
| 817/1 | Mallard | 7½ | 100-125 | 200-250 | 1940-1969 |
| 817/2 | Mallard | 6¾ | 100-125 | 200-250 | 1940-1969 |
| 820 | Pair of Geese | 4 | 25-30 | 50-60 | 1940-1973 |
| 821 | Gosling | 2¼ | 15-20 | 30-40 | 1940-1973 |
| 822 | Gosling | 1¾ | 15-20 | 30-40 | 1940-1973 |
| 827/1 | Goose | 7½ | 80-100 | 160-200 | 1940-1955 |
| 827/2 | Goose | 6 | 75-95 | 150-190 | 1940-1955 |
| 827/3 | Goose | 5 | 70-90 | 140-180 | 1940-1955 |
| 849 | Pheasant (in flight) Wings up | 6 | 85-100 | 175-200 | 1940-1971 |
| 850 | Pheasant (in flight) | 5¾ | 85-100 | 175-200 | 1940-1971 |
| 862 | Fan-Tail Pigeon | — | 100-200 | 225-400 | 1940-1950 |
| ***902 | Mallard | 10 | 50-60 | 100-120 | 1940-1969 |
| 919/1 | Duck | 3¾ | 20-25 | 40-50 | 1941-1969 |
| 919/2 | Duck | 2⅝ | 15-20 | 30-40 | 1941-1969 |
| 919/3 | Duck | 2 | 10-15 | 20-30 | 1941-1969 |
| 925 | Two American Blue Jays | 4¾ | 60-70 | 120-140 | 1941-1965 |
| 926 | Two Baltimore Orioles | 4⅞ | 60-70 | 120-140 | 1941- 1965 |
| 927 | Cockatoo Cardinal | 6 | 50-60 | 100-120 | 1941- 1959 |
| 928 | Tanager (Western) | 6 | 50-60 | 100-120 | 1941-1959 |
| 929 | Chickadee (chestnut backed) | 5¾ | 50-60 | 100-120 | 1941- 1968 |
| 930 | Parakeet | 6 | 50-60 | 100-120 | 1941- 1973 |
| 980 | Robin — 1st version | 3 | 15-20 | 30-40 | 1942-1973 |
| *980 | Robin — re-modelled | 3 | 12·50 | RRP | 1973-C |
| 991 | Chaffinch — 1st version | 2¾ | 15-20 | 30-40 | 1943-1973 |
| *991 | Chaffinch — re-modelled | 2¾ | 12.50 | RRP | 1973-C |
| 992 | Blue Tit — 1st version | 2½ | 15-20 | 20-30 | 1943-1973 |
| *992 | Blue Tit — re-modelled | 2½ | 12·50 | RRP | 1973-C |
| 993 | Wren — 1st version | 2¼ | 15-20 | 30-40 | 1943 -1973 |
| *993 | Wren — re-modelled | 2¼ | 12·50 | RRP | 1973-C |
| 994 | Sheldrake in flight (taking off) | 6 | 95-110 | 200-225 | 1943-1965 |
| 995 | Sheldrake in flight (landing) | 6½ | 95-110 | 200-225 | 1943-1965 |
| 1015 | Two Penguins (courting) | 5½ | 75-90 | 150-185 | 1945-1966 |
| *1018 | Bald Eagle | 7¼ | 50-60 | 100-120 | 1945-1994 |
| 1022 | Two Turtle Doves | 7½ | 150-175 | 300-350 | 1945-1969 |

| Model No | Name of Model | Size inches | Current Value £ | US$ | Production Period |
|---|---|---|---|---|---|
| 1041 | Grey Wagtail — 1st version | 2½ | 15-20 | 30-40 | 1945-1973 |
| *1041 | Grey Wagtail — re-modelled | 2½ | 12·50 | RRP | 1973-C |
| 1042 | Bullfinch — 1st version | 2½ | 15-20 | 30-40 | 1945-1973 |
| *1042 | Bullfinch — re-modelled | 2½ | 12·50 | RRP | 1973-C |
| *1046 | Barn Owl | 7¾ | 32·95 | RRP | 1946-C |
| 1052 | Barnacle Goose | 6½ | 300-400 | 600-800 | 1946-1967 |
| 1159 | Kookaburra | 5¾ | 60-80 | 120-160 | 1949-1976 |
| 1178 | Gouldian Finch (wings out) | 4 | 60-80 | 120-160 | 1949-1959 |
| 1179 | Gouldian Finch (wings in) | 4 | 60-80 | 120-160 | 1949-1959 |
| 1180 | Cockatoo (turquoise/pink or pink/grey) | 8½ | 75-85 | 150-180 | 1949-1975 |
| 1212 | Three Ducks pin tray | 2¾ | 15-20 | 30-40 | 1951-1970 |
| 1216 | Budgerigar (blue) | 7 | 75-85 | 150-170 | 1951-1974 |
| 1216 | Budgerigar (green) | 7 | 175-200 | 350-400 | 1970-1972 |
| 1216 | Budgerigar (yellow) | 7 | 175-200 | 350-400 | 1970-1972 |
| 1217 | Budgerigar (blue) | 7 | 75-85 | 150-170 | 1951-1970 |
| *1218 | Green Woodpecker | 9 | 75-90 | 150-180 | 1951-1989 |
| 1219 | Jay | 6 | 125-150 | 250-300 | 1951-1970 |
| 1225 | Pheasant | 7¾ | 65-85 | 130-170 | 1951-1977 |
| 1226 | Pheasant | 6 | 60-80 | 120-160 | 1951-1977 |
| *1383 | Pigeon (blue or red) | 5½ | 60-80 | 120-160 | 1955-1989 |
| 1413 | Dove (CM series) | 9 | 150-175 | 300-350 | 1956-1965 |
| 1415 | Small Bird (CM series) | 5¾ | 125-150 | 250-300 | 1956-1965 |
| 1416 | Cock (CM series) | 5 | 125-150 | 250-300 | 1956-1965 |
| 1420 | Owl (CM series) | 4¾ | 125-150 | 250-350 | 1956-1965 |
| 1462 | Owl (CM series) | 8¼ | 150-200 | 300-400 | 1956-1965 |
| 1467 | Cock (CM series) | 11¾ | 200-250 | 400-500 | 1956-1965 |
| 1471 | Goose (CM series) | 3¼ | 100-150 | 200-300 | 1957-1963 |
| 1482 | Peacock (CM series) | 3½ | 150-200 | 300-400 | 1957-1965 |
| 1503 | Toucan | — | 100-150 | 200-300 | 1957-1958 |
| 1518/1 | Mallard Duck (Peter Scott) | 2¾ | 75-100 | 150-200 | 1962-1971 |
| 1518/2 | Mallard Duck (Peter Scott) | 2½ | 75-100 | 150-200 | 1962-1971 |
| 1518/3 | Mallard Duck (Peter Scott) | 1⅞ | 60-80 | 120-160 | 1958-1971 |
| 1518/4 | Mallard Duck (Peter Scott) | 1⅝ | 60-80 | 120-160 | 1958-1971 |
| 1519/1 | Mandarin Duck (Peter Scott) | 1⅞ | 60-80 | 120-160 | 1958-1971 |
| 1519/2 | Mandarin Duck (Peter Scott) | 1⅝ | 60-80 | 120-160 | 1958-1971 |
| 1519/3 | Mandarin Duck (Peter Scott) | 1¼ | 60-80 | 120-160 | 1958-1971 |
| 1520/1 | Pochard Duck (Peter Scott) | 1½ | 60-80 | 120-160 | 1958-1971 |
| 1520/2 | Pochard Duck (Peter Scott) | 1¼ | 60-80 | 120-160 | 1958-1971 |
| 1520/3 | Pochard Duck (Peter Scott) | 1 | 60-80 | 120-160 | 1958-1971 |
| 1521 | King Eider Duck (Peter Scott) | 1¾ | 60-80 | 120-160 | 1958-1971 |
| 1522 | Smew Duck (Peter Scott) | 1¼ | 60-80 | 120-160 | 1958-1971 |
| 1523 | Tufted Duck (Peter Scott) | 1¼ | 60-80 | 120-160 | 1958-1971 |
| 1524 | Goldeneye Duck (Peter Scott) | 1⅝ | 60-80 | 120-160 | 1958-1971 |
| 1525 | Goosander Duck (Peter Scott) | 1¾ | 60-80 | 120-160 | 1958-1971 |
| 1526 | Widgeon Duck (Peter Scott) | 1¼ | 60-80 | 120-160 | 1958-1971 |
| 1527 | Shelduck (Peter Scott) | 1⅝ | 60-80 | 120-160 | 1958-1971 |
| 1528 | Shoveller (Peter Scott) | 1⅛ | 60-80 | 120-160 | 1958-1971 |
| 1529 | Teal Duck (Peter Scott) | 1 | 60-80 | 120-160 | 1958-1971 |
| 1614 | Fantail Pigeon | 5 | 150-175 | 300-350 | 1959-1969 |
| 1684 | Swan | 2⅞ | 30-35 | 60-75 | 1960-1970 |
| 1685 | Swan | 2 | 30-35 | 60-75 | 1960-1970 |
| 1686 | Cygnet | 1 | 20-25 | 40-45 | 1960-1970 |
| 1687 | Cygnet | 1 | 20-25 | 40-45 | 1960-1970 |
| 1759 | Pheasant (on thick base) | 5 | 60-80 | 120-160 | 1961-1962 |
| 1774 | Pheasant (on thin base) | 4¾ | 60-80 | 120-160 | 1961-1975 |

| Model No | Name of Model | Size inches | Current Value £ | US$ | Production Period |
|---|---|---|---|---|---|
| 1818 | Cockatoo (turquoise/pink or pink/grey) | 11½ | 100-150 | 200-300 | 1962-1973 |
| 1892 | Leghorn Cockerel | 9 | 150-175 | 300-350 | 1963-1983 |
| 1899 | Sussex Cockerel | 7 | 350-400 | 700-800 | 1963-1970 |
| 1957 | Turkey (white or brown) | 7¼ | 300-350 | 600-700 | 1964-1969 |
| *2026 | Owl | 4⅝ | 14·95 | RRP | 1965-C |
| 2059 | Gamecock | 9½ | 300-350 | 600-700 | 1966-1973 |
| *2062 | Golden Eagle (wings up) | 9½ | 85-100 | 175-200 | 1966-1989 |
| 2063 | Grouse (pair) | 5½ | 300-350 | 600-700 | 1966-1975 |
| 2064 | Partridge (pair) | 5½ | 300-350 | 600-700 | 1966-1975 |
| 2067 | Turkey (miniature) (white or brown) | 2⅜ | 100-125 | 200-250 | 1966-1969 |
| 2071 | Owl (contemporary) | 5⅛ | 45-50 | 90-100 | 1966-1967 |
| 2078 | Pheasants (pair) | 6¾ | 250-300 | 500-600 | 1966-1975 |
| 2105 | Greenfinch — 1st version | 3 | 15-20 | 30-40 | 1967-1973 |
| *2105 | Greenfinch — re-modelled | 3 | 12·50 | RRP | 1973-C |
| 2106 | Whitethroat — 1st version | 2⅞ | 20-25 | 40-50 | 1967-1973 |
| *2106 | Whitethroat — re-modelled | 2⅞ | 15-20 | 30-40 | 1973-1996 |
| *2183 | Baltimore Oriole | 3⅞ | 75-100 | 150-200 | 1970-1973 |
| *2184 | Cedar Wax-wing | 4⅝ | 75-100 | 150-200 | 1970-1973 |
| *2187 | American Robin | 4⅛ | 75-100 | 150-200 | 1970-1973 |
| *2188 | Blue Jay | 4⅜ | 75-100 | 150-200 | 1970-1973 |
| *2189 | Black Capped Chickadee | 4½ | 75-100 | 150-200 | 1970-1973 |
| *2190 | Evening Crosbeak | 4 | 75-100 | 150-200 | 1970-1973 |
| *2191 | Quail | 4⅞ | 75-100 | 150-200 | 1970-1973 |
| **2238 | Owl ('Moda' Range) | 6¾ | 45-50 | 90-100 | 1968-1971 |
| **2239 | Bird ('Moda' Range) | 5 | 45-50 | 90-100 | 1968-1971 |
| **2240 | Cock ('Moda' Range) | 6 | 45-50 | 90-100 | 1968-1971 |
| *2273 | Goldfinch | 3 | 20-25 | 40-50 | 1969-1995 |
| *2274 | Stonechat | 3 | 12·50 | RRP | 1969-C |
| *2305 | Magpie | 5 | 75-100 | 150-200 | 1970-1982 |
| 2307 | Eagle on Rock (wings out) | 3¾ | 50-75 | 100-150 | 1970-1975 |
| *2308 | Song Thrush | 5¾ | 75-100 | 150-200 | 1970-1989 |
| *2315 | Cuckoo | 5 | 75-100 | 150-200 | 1970-1982 |
| *2316 | Kestrel | 6¾ | 75-100 | 150-200 | 1970-1989 |
| 2357 | Penguin – standing | 12 | 250-300 | 500-600 | 1971-1975 |
| **2359 | Stork (black) | 10½ | 40-50 | 80-100 | 1971-1972 |
| *2371 | Kingfisher | 5 | 32·95 | RRP | 1971-C |
| 2398 | Penguin baby standing | 6⅞ | 150-200 | 325-450 | 1972-1975 |
| 2399 | Penguin chick | 6¾ | 150-200 | 325-450 | 1972-1973 |
| *2413 | Nuthatch | 3 | 20-25 | 40-50 | 1972-1995 |
| *2415 | Gold Crest | 2⅝ | 12·50 | RRP | 1972-C |
| *2416 | Lapwing | 5⅜ | 75-100 | 150-200 | 1972-1982 |
| *2417 | Jay | 5⅛ | 75-100 | 150-200 | 1972-1982 |
| *2420 | Lesser Spotted Woodpecker | 5½ | 75-100 | 150-200 | 1972-1982 |
| 2434 | Penguin baby sliding | 8 long | 150-200 | 350-425 | 1972-1975 |
| 2579 | Kingfisher (not put into production) | 3 | 75-100 | 150-200 | 1977 only |
| **2760 | Pheasant | 10½ | 125-150 | 250-300 | 1981-1990 |
| 3272 | Tawny Owl | 3½ | 12·50 | RRP | 1991-C |
| 3273 | Barn Owl | 3½ | 12·50 | RRP | 1991-C |
| 3274 | Great Tit | 3 | 15-20 | | 1991-1995 |
| 3275 | Kingfisher | 3 | 12·50 | RRP | 1991-C |

*Available in gloss or matt finish
** Matt finish only   *** makes set of five with model No. 756
C=Current

# Bird Wall Plaques

(All models carry the Beswick mark)

| Model No | Name of Model | Size inches | Current Value £ | US$ | Production Period |
|---|---|---|---|---|---|
| 572 | Bird on Bush | 7 x 4¼ | 75-100 | 150-200 | 1938-1954 |
| 574 | Three Blue Tits | 9¾ x 5 | 75-100 | 150-200 | 1938-1954 |
| 596/0 | Mallard | 11¾ | 35-45 | 70-90 | 1938-1971 |
| 596/1 | Mallard | 10 | 35-40 | 70-80 | 1938-1973 |
| 596/2 | Mallard | 8¾ | 30-35 | 60-70 | 1938-1973 |
| 596/3 | Mallard | 7 | 25-30 | 50-60 | 1938-1973 |
| 596/4 | Mallard | 5¾ | 20-25 | 40-50 | 1938-1971 |
| *658/1 | Seagull | 14 | 40-45 | 80-90 | 1938-1967 |
| *658/2 | Seagull | 11¾ | 35-40 | 70-80 | 1938-1967 |
| *658/3 | Seagull | 10⅛ | 30-35 | 60-70 | 1938-1967 |
| *658/4 | Seagull | 8 | 25-30 | 50-60 | 1938-1967 |
| *661/1 | Pheasant | 12 | 40-45 | 80-90 | 1938-1971 |
| *661/2 | Pheasant | 10½ | 35-40 | 70-80 | 1938-1971 |
| *661/3 | Pheasant | 8½ | 30-35 | 60-70 | 1938-1971 |
| *705 | Blue Tit (facing right) | 4½ | 35-40 | 70-80 | 1939-1967 |
| *706 | Blue Tit (facing left) | 4½ | 35-40 | 70-80 | 1939-1967 |
| *707 | Blue Tit (wings up) | 4½ | 35-40 | 70-80 | 1939-1967 |
| *729/1 | Kingfisher | 7½ | 40-45 | 80-90 | 1939-1971 |
| *729/2 | Kingfisher | 6 | 35-40 | 70-80 | 1939-1971 |
| *729/3 | Kingfisher | 5 | 30-35 | 60-70 | 1939-1971 |
| 731 | Flamingo | 15 long | 175-200 | 350-400 | 1939-1955 |
| **743 | Kingfisher | 6 | 50-60 | 100-120 | 1939-1955 |
| *757/1 | Swallow | 6 | 35-40 | 70-80 | 1939-1973 |
| *757/2 | Swallow | 5 | 30-35 | 60-70 | 1939-1973 |
| *757/3 | Swallow | 4 | 25-30 | 50-60 | 1939-1973 |
| 922/1 | Seagull | 12 | 40-45 | 80-90 | 1941-1971 |
| 922/2 | Seagull | 10½ | 35-40 | 70-80 | 1941-1971 |
| 922/3 | Seagull | 9½ | 30-35 | 60-70 | 1941-1971 |
| 1023/1 | Humming Bird | 5¾ | 75-100 | 150-200 | 1945-1967 |
| 1023/2 | Humming Bird | 5 | 60-80 | 120-160 | 1945-1967 |
| 1023/3 | Humming Bird | 4½ | 50-60 | 100-120 | 1945-1967 |
| 1188/1 | Pink Legged Partridge | 10½ | 75-100 | 150-200 | 1950-1967 |
| 1188/2 | Pink Legged Partridge | 9 | 60-80 | 120-160 | 1950-1967 |
| 1188/3 | Pink Legged Partridge | 7½ | 50-60 | 100-120 | 1950-1967 |
| 1344/1 | Green Woodpecker | 7½ | 75-100 | 150-200 | 1954-1967 |
| 1344/2 | Green Woodpecker | 6 | 60-80 | 120-160 | 1954-1967 |
| 1344/3 | Green Woodpecker | 5 | 50-60 | 100-120 | 1954-1967 |
| 1530/1 | Teal | 8¼ | 80-100 | 160-200 | 1958-1967 |
| 1530/2 | Teal | 7¼ | 70-80 | 140-160 | 1958-1967 |
| 1530/3 | Teal | 6¼ | 60-70 | 120-140 | 1958-1967 |

* Available in gloss or matt glaze
**Pairs with 729/2 but flying in opposite direction

# Butterfly Plaques

(All models carry the Beswick mark)
A small number of delightful butterfly wall plaques were modelled by Albert Hallam, early in 1957. These are difficult to find, so it would seem that only a small number were produced. They are also easily damaged and therefore collectors must pay careful attention to condition.

| Model No | Name of Model | Size inches | Current Value £ | US$ | Production Period |
|---|---|---|---|---|---|
| 1487 | Purple Emperor (large) | 7 x 3½ | 175-200 | 350-425 | 1957-1960 |
| 1488 | Red Admiral (large) | 7 x 3½ | 175-200 | 350-425 | 1957-1960 |
| 1489 | Peacock (large) | 7 x 3½ | 175-200 | 350-425 | 1957-1960 |
| 1490 | Clouded Yellow (medium) | 5¼ x 3½ | 150-175 | 300-350 | 1957-1960 |
| 1491 | Large Tortoiseshell (medium) | 5¼ x 3½ | 150-175 | 300-350 | 1957-1960 |
| 1492 | Swallow Tail (medium) | 5¼ x 3½ | 150-175 | 300-350 | 1957-1960 |
| 1493 | Small Copper (small) | 3¾ x 2¼ | 125-150 | 150-300 | 1957-1960 |
| 1494 | Purple Hairstreak (small) | 3¾ x 2¼ | 125-150 | 150-300 | 1957-1960 |
| 1495 | Small Heath (small) | 3¾ x 2¼ | 125-150 | 150-300 | 1957-1960 |

# Cats

(All current cats produced since August 1989 carry a Royal Doulton backstamp)
The Beswick collection includes all types of cats from mischievous moggies to sleek pedigrees. As several of the Beswick modellers have been commissioned to submit cat models over the years, the cat enthusiast can acquire an interesting and stylistically varied collection. A kitten wearing a bow featured in the Beswick catalogues at the turn of the century but no more cats appeared until 1945. Since then, they have been consistently popular.

Miss Granoska's pair of Siamese kittens, for example, which was first introduced in 1953, is still being made today. Another long term favourite is the Fireside model, also a Siamese, which was introduced in 1967. Siamese and Persians tend to be the most popular of all the breeds, certainly they are the best represented at cat shows, and this is borne out by the current collection of pedigree models.

Beswick artists have also enjoyed putting cats in humorous situations curled up on a chimney pot or playing a musical instrument and these are featured in the comic animals section.

More recently they have featured on some of the catalogue specials, along with other animals.

I think that the variety of decorations, found on models produced during the late 1960s make cats very collectable and I have found it very difficult to price them satisfactorily. The availability of these different decorations, with the Beswick mark, on some models which have also carried the Doulton mark since 1989, makes the price range much greater than I would like and you must make your own final decision on what to pay for any particular model which you see.

29

| Model No | Name of Model | Height inches | Current Value £ | US$ | DA No | Production Period |
|---|---|---|---|---|---|---|
| ø1030 | Cat – sitting | $6\frac{1}{4}$ | 50-150 | 100-300 | | 1945-1973 |
| ø1031 | Cat – sitting | $4\frac{1}{2}$ | 50-150 | 100-300 | | 1945-1973 |
| ***1296 | Siamese Kittens – lying | $2\frac{3}{4}$ | 10·75 | RRP | 122 | 1953-C |
| ø1316 | Persian Kittens – sitting | $3\frac{1}{2}$ | 40-60 | 80-120 | | 1953-1973 |
| 1412 | Cat (CM series) – sitting | $9\frac{5}{8}$ | 125-150 | 250-300 | | 1956-1965 |
| 1417 | Kitten (CM series) – sitting | $5\frac{5}{8}$ | 100-125 | 200-250 | | 1956-1965 |
| 1435 | Cat – sitting | $5\frac{1}{4}$ | 100-150 | 200-300 | | 1956-1961 |
| ø1436 | Kitten – sitting | $3\frac{1}{4}$ | 8·50 | RRP | 123 | 1956-C |
| 1437 | Cat — lying (small) | $2\frac{3}{4}$ | 150-200 | 300-400 | | 1956-1961 |
| 1438 | Cat — standing (large) | — | 150-200 | 300-400 | | 1956-1961 |
| 1474 | Cat (CM series) – sitting | $5\frac{1}{4}$ | 100-125 | 200-250 | | 1957-1965 |
| 1541 | Cat (large) – sitting | — | 150-200 | 300-400 | | 1958-1960 |
| 1542 | Cat – lying | — | 100-125 | 200-250 | | 1958-1960 |
| 1543 | Cat – sitting | 3 | 100-125 | 200-250 | | 1958-1960 |
| ***1558 | Siamese – lying | $7\frac{1}{4}$ | 15·95 | RRP | 124 | 1958-C |
| ***1559 | Siamese – lying | $7\frac{1}{4}$ | 15·95 | RRP | 125 | 1958-C |
| *1560 | Cat – sitting | $10\frac{3}{4}$ | 100-125 | 200-150 | | 1958-1966 |
| *1561 | Cat – sitting | $10\frac{3}{4}$ | 100-125 | 200-150 | | 1958-1966 |
| **1677 | Cat climbing (part of set see 1678 Wild Animals) | $7\frac{1}{2}$ | 13·95 | RRP | | 1960-C |
| 1803 | Cat singing (part of Bedtime Chorus set see Figures) | $1\frac{1}{2}$ | 45-50 | 90-100 | | 1962-1971 |
| 1857 | Kitten climbing | | 45-50 | 90-100 | | 1963-1964 |
| ø1867 | Persian Cat – sitting | $8\frac{1}{2}$ | 30-130 | 60-275 | 126 | 1963-1996 |
| ø1876 | Persian Cat – lying | $3\frac{1}{2}$ | 100-150 | 200-300 | | 1963-1971 |
| ø1877 | Persian Cat – sitting | $6\frac{1}{2}$ | 100-150 | 200-300 | | 1963-1971 |
| ø1880 | Persian Cat – sitting | $5\frac{1}{4}$ | 100-150 | 200-300 | | 1963-1971 |
| ***1882 | Siamese Cat – sitting | $9\frac{1}{2}$ | 50-75 | 100-150 | 127 | 1963-1994 |
| ø1883 | Persian Cat – sitting up (paw up) | $6\frac{1}{2}$ | 100-150 | 200-300 | | 1963-1971 |
| ø1885 | Persian Kitten – standing | $4\frac{3}{4}$ | 100-150 | 200-300 | | 1963-1972 |
| ø1886 | Persian Kitten – sitting | 4 | 10.75 | RRP | 128 | 1963-C |
| ***1887 | Siamese Cat – sitting | $4\frac{1}{8}$ | 9·95 | RRP | 129 | 1963-C |
| ***1897 | Siamese Cat – standing | $6\frac{1}{2}$ | 19·95 | RRP | 130 | 1963-C |
| ***1897 | Cat (black) – standing | $6\frac{1}{2}$ | 30-35 | 60-70 | 131 | 1987-1994 |
| ø1898 | Persian Cat – standing (long hair) | 5 | 30-100 | 60-150 | 132 | 1963-1994 |
| ***2139 | Siamese Fireside Cat – sitting | $13\frac{3}{4}$ | 75-100 | 150-200 | 83 | 1967-1996 |
| 2301 | Cat climbing (part of set see 2302 Wild Animals) | $4\frac{1}{2}$ | 40-50 | 80-100 | | 1970-1971 |
| 2311 | Siamese Cat (miniature) | $1\frac{1}{2}$ | 40-50 | 80-100 | | 1970-1971 |

C=Current
*Available facing left or right and decorated white (Zodiac signs) or black (plain). Also available as a lamp.
**Currently still carries a Beswick backstamp.
***Available in gloss or matt finish
ø Can be found in grey, white or ginger with gloss or matt finish.
Also in tabby 'Swiss-roll' and ginger 'Swiss roll', gloss finish only
Note: The distinctive 'Swiss roll' decoration only appears to have been available from the mid to late 1960s. It is interesting to note that for one year only, 1965, the following were available in blue: 1867/1876/1877/1880/1883/1885/1886/1898.

# Connoisseur Series

(All current models carry a Royal Doulton backstamp)
The models in this series of animal and bird studies form a highly specialised branch of the potters art, with a long and distinguished tradition to follow.

The series falls into five distinct groups — Cattle, Horses, Dogs, Wildlife Animals and Birds — and most of these are available on a polished wood base some with an inscribed metal plate giving a description of the model and all having a matt finish, except 2431, which is gloss only.

Each piece represents a completely natural study and captures all the grace, strength and bearing of the real animal or bird portrayed. Every muscle, feather and feature is accurate and the finished models are a tribute to the skills and knowledge of the John Beswick Studio sculptors and artists.

The series was introduced in 1967 with a very detailed model of the racehorse 'Arkle' (2065) owned by Anne, Duchess of Westminster and trained by Mr T. Dreaper in Ireland. The horse was mounted on a hardwood base and was the forerunner of many more finely detailed models.

The success of this initial model prompted Beswick to widen the scope of the series and a number of earlier models, already in production, were then added to the series, wood bases being used as appropriate.

| Model No | Name of Model | Height inches | Current Value £ | US$ | DA No | Production Period |
|---|---|---|---|---|---|---|
| ***998 | Elephant | 10¼ | 150-200 | 300-400 | | 1971-1975 |
| *1265 | Arab Xayal Horse | 7⅛ | 60-80 | 130-150 | | 1971-1989 |
| *1363 | Hereford Bull | 5⅜ | 100-110 | 200-225 | | 1971-1975 |
| *1439 | Friesan Bull | 5⅝ | 100-110 | 200-225 | | 1971-1975 |
| *1564 | Racehorse | 12⅛ | 80-100 | 150-200 | | 1971-1980 |
| ***1702 | Puma tawny | 8½ | 100-120 | 200-250 | | 1960-1989 |
| *1734 | Hunter dapple | 12⅛ | 100-120 | 200-250 | | 1971-1983 |
| ***1770 | Indian Elephant | 12 | 150-200 | 300-400 | | 1971-1982 |
| *1771 | Arab dapple | 8⅛ | 90-100 | 175-200 | | 1971-1989 |
| *1772 | Thoroughbred Horse | 8⅞ | 60-80 | 120-160 | | 1971-1989 |
| *1933 | Beagle 'Wendover Billy' | 5⅞ | 60-80 | 120-160 | | 1971-1989 |
| *2045 | Basset Hound 'Fochno Trinket' | 5⅞ | 60-80 | 120-160 | | 1971-1989 |
| ***2062 | Golden Eagle | 9½ | 100-125 | 200-250 | | 1966-1989 |
| *2065 | 'Arkle' racehorse | 11⅞ | 155·00 | RRP | 15 | 1966-C |
| *2084 | 'Arkle' Pat Taaffe up | 12⅝ | 275-325 | 550-650 | | 1966-1980 |
| *2210 | Highwayman on horse | 13⅞ | 600-800 | 1200-1600 | | 1968-1975 |
| *2269 | Arab Stallion with authentic saddle | 9½ | 500-600 | 1000-1200 | | 1969-1973 |
| *2275 | Bedouin Arab on horse | 11½ | 800-1000 | 1600-2000 | | 1969-1973 |
| ***2309 | Shire Horse | 10¾ | 60-80 | 120-160 | | 1970-1982 |
| *2340 | 'Cardigan Bay' racehorse | 9¼ | 400-500 | 800-1000 | | 1970-1976 |
| *2345 | 'Nijinsky' racehorse | 11⅛ | 155·00 | RRP | 16 | 1970-C |
| *2352 | 'Nijinsky' – Lester Piggott up | 12⅝ | 275-325 | 550-650 | | 1971-1982 |
| *2422 | 'Mill Reef' racehorse | 9 | 100-125 | 200-250 | | 1972-1989 |
| *2431 | Mountie Stallion | 10 | 400-500 | 800-1000 | | 1973 only |
| *2463 | Charolais Bull | 5⅜ | 100-125 | 220-250 | | 1975-1979 |
| *2466/ 2536 | 'Black Beauty' & foal | 7¾ | 89·95 | RRP | 17 | 1973-C |
| *2510 | 'Red Rum' racehorse | 12½ | 155·00 | RRP | 18 | 1974-C |

| Model No | Name of Model | Height inches | Current Value £ | US$ | DA No | Production Period |
|---|---|---|---|---|---|---|
| *2511 | 'Red Rum' – Brian Fletcher up | 13 | 275-325 | 550-650 | | 1974-1983 |
| *2535 | 'Psalm' Ann Moore up | 12¾ | 275-325 | 550-650 | | 1975-1982 |
| *2540 | 'Psalm' racehorse | 11½ | 175-200 | 350-400 | | 1975-1982 |
| *2541 | Welsh Mountain Pony | 9 | 200-250 | 400-500 | | 1975-1989 |
| *2542 | Hereford Bull | 7½ | 100-125 | 100-250 | 19 | 1975-1996 |
| 2554 | Lion on rock | 8¼ | 80-100 | 160-200 | | 1975-1983 |
| *2558 | 'Grundy' racehorse | 11¼ | 155·00 | RRP | 20 | 1976-C |
| *2562 | Lifeguard on horse | 14½ | 400-450 | 800-900 | 22 | 1976-1996 |
| *2574 | Polled Hereford Bull | 7½ | 100-125 | 200-250 | 21 | 1976-1996 |
| *2580 | Friesian Bull | 7⅜ | 140·00 | RRP | 23 | 1976-C |
| *2581 | Collie | 8¼ | 60-80 | 120-160 | 24 | 1976-1994 |
| *2582 | Blues and Royals (mounted) | 14½ | 400-450 | 800-900 | 25 | 1987-1996 |
| *2587 | Alsatian | 8⅞ | 60-80 | 120-160 | 26 | 1977-1994 |
| *2600 | Charolais Bull | 7½ | 100-125 | 200-250 | 27 | 1977-1996 |
| *2605 | Morgan Horse | 11½ | 100-125 | 200-250 | 28 | 1977-1996 |
| 2607 | Friesian Cow | 7½ | 140·00 | RRP | 29 | 1977-C |
| *2607/ 2690 | Friesian Cow & calf | 7½ | 159·00 | RRP | 30 | 1980-C |
| *2608 | 'The Minstrel' racehorse | 13½ | 155·00 | RRP | 31 | 1978-C |
| **2629 | Stag | 13½ | 80-100 | 160-200 | 32 | 1978-1996 |
| *2648/ 2652 | Charolais Cow & calf | 7¼ | 100-125 | 200-250 | 33 | 1979-1996 |
| *2667/ 2669 | Hereford Cow & calf | 7 | 100-125 | 200-250 | 34 | 1980-1996 |
| 2671 | 'Moonlight' horse | 11¼ | 80-100 | 160-200 | 35 | 1980-1996 |
| 2671 | 'Sunburst' horse | 11¼ | 80-100 | 160-200 | 36 | 1986-1995 |
| **2671 | 'Nightshade' horse | 11¼ | 80-100 | 160-200 | 35 | 1986-1996 |
| *2674 | 'Troy' racehorse | 11¾ | 155·00 | RRP | 37 | 1980-C |
| **2725 | Cheetah on rock | 6½ | 100-125 | 200-250 | 39 | 1981-1994 |
| **2760 | Pheasant | 10½ | 100-125 | 200-250 | 38 | 1981-1994 |

*Mounted on polished wooden base.
**On wooden base from 1990
***Available in gloss or matt
NOTES:
2629 Stag is also called Majestic Stag
2671 Nightshade is also called Champion
2725 Cheetah on Rock is also called The Watering Hole
2760 Pheasant is also called Open Ground (all with re-modelled bases)

# Colin Melbourne Models

Beswick were always interested in new ideas and when Mr Melbourne visited the factory, in 1955, he talked to Mr Ewart Beswick, Chairman and Managing Director, about his ideas on 'modern' ceramics.

Ewart offered him employment and this gave him the opportunity to design and model a contemporary collection.

He was given his own studio and showroom within the factory and this included a special decorating and glazing department. The collection which followed was approved by the Design Council and were known as the 'CM Series)' and intended to match the contemporary scene.

Despite being of limited commercial success, these very good sculptural forms were well produced and offered at very competitive prices. Today, they form a very collectable series.

| Model No | Name of Model | Size inches | Current Value £ | US$ | Production Period |
|---|---|---|---|---|---|
| 1409 | Bison (large) | 10½ | 200-250 | 400-500 | 1956-1963 |
| 1410 | Cow | 7⅛ | 150-200 | 300-400 | 1956-1961 |
| 1411 | Horse | 8¾ | 150-200 | 300-400 | 1956-1971 |
| 1412 | Cat (large) – sitting | 9⅝ | 250-300 | 500-600 | 1956-1965 |
| 1413 | Dove | 9 | 150-175 | 300-350 | 1956-1965 |
| 1414 | Bison (medium) | 8¾ | 150-200 | 300-400 | 1956-1970 |
| 1415 | Bird (small) | 5¾ | 125-150 | 250-300 | 1956-1965 |
| 1416 | Cockerel (small) | 5 | 125-150 | 250-300 | 1956-1965 |
| 1417 | Kitten – sitting | 5⅝ | 150-200 | 300-400 | 1956-1965 |
| 1418 | Fox (small) | 8 long | 150-200 | 300-400 | 1956-1970 |
| 1419 | Lion | 5¼ | 200-250 | 400-500 | 1956-1962 |
| 1420 | Owl (small) | 4¾ | 125-150 | 250-300 | 1956-1965 |
| 1462 | Owl (large) | 8¼ | 150-200 | 300-400 | 1956-1965 |
| 1463 | Bulldog – standing | 3¾ | 125-150 | 250-300 | 1956-1963 |
| 1465 | Zebra | 6 | 150-200 | 300-400 | 1956-1970 |
| 1467 | Cockerel (large) | 11¾ | 200-250 | 400-500 | 1956-1965 |
| 1468 | Bison (small) | — | 100-150 | 200-300 | 1956-1970 |
| 1469 | Dachshund – standing | 3¼ | 125-150 | 250-300 | 1957-1965 |
| 1470 | Clown on horse (small) | 5¾ | 200-250 | 400-500 | 1957-1963 |
| 1471 | Goose | 3¼ | 100-150 | 200-300 | 1957-1963 |
| 1472 | Poodle – standing | 5¾ | 125-150 | 250-300 | 1957-1963 |
| 1473 | Pig | 2½ | 125-150 | 250-300 | 1957-1966 |
| 1474 | Cat (small) – sitting | 5¼ | 200-250 | 400-500 | 1957-1965 |
| 1475 | Fox (large) | 10 long | 200-250 | 400-500 | 1957-1970 |
| 1476 | Clown on horse (large) | 8½ | 250-300 | 500-600 | 1957-1963 |
| 1481 | Reindeer | 5½ | 250-300 | 500-600 | 1957-1970 |
| 1482 | Peacock | 3½ | 150-200 | 300-400 | 1957-1965 |

*All models should be marked 'CM' but many are not. Several different styles of decoration will be found for each piece.*

# Dogs

(All current models carry a Beswick backstamp unless allocated a 'DA' number. These are backstamped Royal Doulton)

There is no doubt that the dog is man's best friend whether it be as a hunter, guard or, most commonly, a companion. Always ready for a game or a walk and only asking for food and a bed, he amply repays all the love and attention given to him.

As early as 1898, Beswick had introduced models of dogs as mantlepiece ornaments. These Old English Dogs are still made today and are very popular. Since 1934, over a hundred dogs have appeared in the pattern books from frisky mongrels to pedigree show dogs. According to the Kennel Club there are approximately seventy different species of dog and about two hundred varieties in all, so there is still plenty of scope for the Beswick modellers.

A problem with selecting a champion dog is that breeders have different conceptions of the true characteristics of a winner or top dog, thus it is a challenge to achieve a model which is approved by all. The very best of the championship winners are singled out to pose for Beswick, with a team of experts advising on the final product. Crufts judges, for example, assess the clay reproduction and suggest improvements until satisfied that the 'conformation' is exact. Few potteries can compete against such high standards.

| Model No | Name of Model | Height inches | Current Value £ | US$ | DA No | Production Period |
|---|---|---|---|---|---|---|
| 171 | Dog – begging | 4¾ | 40-50 | 80-95 | | 1934-1954 |
| 286 | Dog – sitting | 6 | 30-40 | 60-80 | | 1934-1959 |
| 301 | Sealyham plaque (with bow) | 7½ | 60-80 | 120-160 | | 1935-1940 |
| 302 | Sealyham – standing | 5¾ | 40-50 | 80-95 | | 1935-1959 |
| 307 | Sealyham plaque (without bow) | 7½ | 60-80 | 120-160 | | 1935-1940 |
| †††308 | Sealyham – sitting | 6 | 40-50 | 80-95 | | 1935-1959 |
| 361 | Dachshund (pointed ears) | 5½ | 40-50 | 80-95 | | 1936-1956 |
| øø361 | Dachshund (rounded ears) | 5½ | 40-50 | 80-95 | | 1956-1982 |
| 373 | Sealyham plaque (with bow) | 7 | 60-80 | 120-160 | | 1936-1940 |
| 453 | Old English Sheep Dog – sitting | 8½ | 80-100 | 160-200 | | 1936-1973 |
| ø454 | Dog sitting (lollopy) | 4¼ | 30-40 | 60-80 | | 1936-1969 |
| 668 | Dog plaque | 10 x 11 | 100-120 | 200-250 | | 1938-1962 |
| 752 | Scottie (as 87 ashtray) | — | 25-30 | 50-60 | | 1939-1954 |
| 753 | Sealyham | — | 25-30 | 50-60 | | 1939-1954 |
| 810 | Bulldog ash tray (sailors hat) | 4 | 60-80 | 120-160 | | 1940-1954 |
| 869 | Five dogs ash tray | 2 | 20-25 | 40-50 | | 1940-1968 |
| 916 | Three dogs ash tray | 2 | 15-20 | 30-40 | | 1941-1968 |
| 917 | Three dogs (as 916 ash tray) | 2 | 15-20 | 30-40 | | 1941-1965 |
| **941 | Foxhound (see 2263) | 2⅞ | 15-20 | 30-40 | | 1941-1969 |
| **942 | Foxhound (see 2265) | 2¾ | 15-20 | 30-40 | | 1941-1969 |
| **943 | Foxhound (see 2264) | 2⅞ | 15-20 | 30-40 | | 1941-1969 |
| **944 | Foxhound (see 2262) | 2½ | 15-20 | 30-40 | | 1941-1969 |
| ***961 | Dalmation 'Arnoldene' | 5¾ | 35-40 | 70-80 | | 1941-1993 |
| 962 | Airedale 'Cast Iron Monarch' | 5½ | 35-40 | 70-80 | | 1941-1989 |
| 963 | Wire-haired Fox Terrier 'Talavera Romulus' | 5¾ | 35-40 | 70-80 | | 1941-1983 |
| 964 | Smooth Fox Terrier 'Endon Black Rod' | 5½ | 80-100 | 160-200 | | 1941-1968 |
| 965 | Bulldog 'Basford British Mascot' | 5½ | 40-50 | 80-95 | | 1941-1989 |
| 966 | Irish Setter 'Sugar of Wendover' | 5¾ | 35-40 | 70-80 | | 1941-1989 |
| ††967 | Cocker Spaniel 'Horseshoe Primular' | 5¾ | 35-40 | 70-80 | | 1941-1993 |
| 968 | Great Dane 'Ruler of Oubourgh' | 7 | 40-50 | 80-95 | | 1941-1993 |
| ***969 | Alsatian – 'Ulrica of Brittas' | 5¾ | 40-50 | 80-95 | | 1942-1993 |
| 970 | Bull Terrier– 'Romany Rhinestone' (brindle or white) | 5⅝ | 40-60 | 80-120 | | 1942-1993 |
| 971 | Sealyham 'Forestedge Foxglove' | 4 | 80-100 | 160-200 | | 1942-1967 |
| ***972 | Greyhound 'Jovial Rodger' | 6 | 40-60 | 80-120 | | 1942-1989 |
| 973 | English Setter 'Bayledone Baronet' | 5½ | 35-40 | 70-80 | | 1942-1989 |
| 1055 | Cairn Terrier with ball | 4 | 40-50 | 80-95 | | 1946-1969 |
| 1057 | Spaniel running | 3¾ | 40-60 | 80-120 | | 1946-1967 |
| 1059 | Pekinese begging | 4¼ | 40-50 | 80-95 | | 1946-1967 |
| 1060 | Red Setter lying down | 3 | 40-60 | 80-120 | | 1946-1962 |
| 1061 | Sealyham lying down | 2 | 40-50 | 80-95 | | 1946-1962 |
| 1062 | Wire haired terrier walking | 4 | 40-50 | 80-95 | | 1946-1962 |
| 1202 | Boxer 'Blue Moutain Greta' (Brindle or brown) | 5½ | 40-50 | 80-95 | | 1950-1988 |
| 1220 | English Setter (large) | 8 | 80-100 | 160-200 | | 1951-1967 |
| 1239 | Dog begging (from model 1086) | 2½ | 40-50 | 80-95 | | 1952-1967 |
| 1240 | Dog sitting (from model 1096) | 2⅛ | 40-50 | 80-95 | | 1952-1967 |
| 1241 | Dog howling (from model 909) | 1¼ | 40-50 | 80-95 | | 1952-1967 |
| 1242 | Dog barking (from model 906) | 1⅛ | 40-50 | 80-95 | | 1952-1967 |
| 1294 | Poodle (black or white) 'Ebonit Av Barbette'' | — | 125-175 | 250-350 | | 1953-1967 |

| Model No | Name of Model | Height inches | Current Value £ | US$ | DA No | Production Period |
|---|---|---|---|---|---|---|
| 1299 | Corgi 'Black Prince (black & tan or fawn) | 5⅝ | 35-40 | 70-80 | | 1953-1993 |
| †1378/1 | Old English Dog | 13¼ | 60-80 | 120-160 | | 1955-1976 |
| †1378/2 | Old English Dog | 11½ | 60-80 | 120-160 | | 1955-1972 |
| †1378/3 | Old English Dog | 10 | 79·95≠ | RRP | 89/90 | 1955-C |
| †1378/4 | Old English Dog | 9 | 39·95≠ | RRP | 91/92 | 1955-C |
| †1378/5 | Old English Dog | 7½ | 29·95≠ | RRP | 93/94 | 1955-C |
| †1378/6 | Old English Dog | 5½ | 23·95≠ | RRP | 95/96 | 1955-C |
| †1378/7 | Old English Dog | 3½ | 15·95≠ | RRP | 97/98 | 1955-C |
| ****1386 | Poodle (black, white, brown or honey) | 3½ | 20-25 | 40-50 | | 1955-1989 |
| ****1460 | Dachshund – sitting (black & tan or tan) | 2¾ | 12·95 | RRP | | 1956-C |
| 1461 | Dachshund begging (black & tan or tan) | 4 | 20-25 | 40-50 | | 1957-1980 |
| 1463 | Bulldog (CM series) – standing | 3¾ | 125-150 | 250-300 | | 1956-1963 |
| 1469 | Dachshund (CM series) – standing | 3¼ | 125-150 | 250-300 | | 1957-1965 |
| 1472 | Poodle (CM series) – standing | 5¾ | 125-150 | 250-300 | | 1957-1963 |
| ***1548 | Labrador 'Solomon of Wendover'(black or golden) | 5½ | 30-35 | 60-70 | | 1958-1993 |
| ****1731 | Bulldog 'Bosun' | 2½ | 12·95 | RRP | | 1960-C |
| ****1736 | Corgi | 2¾ | 15-20 | 30-40 | | 1961-1996 |
| 1753 | Bull Terrier | 3½ | 60-80 | 120-160 | | 1961-1971 |
| ****1754 | Cocker Spaniel (liver & white or black & white) | 3 | 12.95 | RRP | | 1961-C |
| 1762 | Alsatian | 3¼ | 25-30 | 50-60 | | 1961-1970 |
| ****1763 | Dalmatian | 3½ | 12·95 | RRP | | 1961-C |
| 1786/1 | Whippet 'Winged Foot Marksman of Allways' (tail curved down between legs) | 4½ | 60-80 | 120-160 | | 1961-1983 |
| 1786/2 | Whippet 'Winged Foot Marksman of Allways' (tail attached to back leg) | 4½ | 50-60 | 100-120 | | 1983-1989 |
| ***1791 | Collie 'Lochinvar of Ladypark' | 5¾ | 30-35 | 60-70 | | 1961-1993 |
| 1792 | Sheep Dog | 5½ | 30-35 | 60-70 | | 1961-1993 |
| 1814 | Collie | 3¼ | 30-35 | 60-70 | | 1962-1975 |
| 1824 | Small dog singing (part of Bedtime Chorus Set — see Figures) | 1⅜ | 40-50 | 95-100 | | 1962-1971 |
| 1852 | Boxer | 3 | 40-60 | 80-120 | | 1962-1975 |
| ****1854 | Sheep Dog | 3 | 13·95 | RRP | | 1962-C |
| 1855 | Retriever | 3¼ | 40-50 | 80-95 | | 1962-1975 |
| 1871 | Dubonnet Poodle | 4⅛ | 60-80 | 120-160 | | 1963-1967 |
| 1872 | Dubonnet Bulldog | 3¾ | 60-80 | 120-160 | | 1963-1967 |
| 1932/1460 | Dachshund on ash tray | 5 | 30-35 | 60-70 | | 1962-1969 |
| 1933 | Beagle 'Wendover Billy' | 5 | 30-35 | 60-70 | | 1964-1989 |
| ****1939 | Beagle 'Wendover Billy' | 3 | 13·95 | RRP | | 1964-C |
| 1944 | Yorkshire Terrier | 3½ | 40-50 | 80-95 | | 1964-1975 |
| ****1956 | Labrador (Golden or Black) | 3¼ | 9·95 | RRP | | 1964-C |
| 1982 | Staffordshire Bull Terrier 'Bandits Brintiga' | 4¾ | 125-175 | 250-350 | | 1964-1969 |
| ***1997 | Pug 'Cutmil Cupie' | 4½ | 40-50 | 80-95 | | 1965-1982 |
| ****1998 | Pug 'Cutmil Cupie' | 2½ | 30-40 | 60-80 | | 1966-1989 |
| 2023 | Jack Russell Terrier | 5 | 30-40 | 60-80 | | 1965-1993 |
| 2037 | Scottie | 4½ | 30-40 | 60-80 | | 1965-1989 |
| 2038 | West Highland Terrier | 4¾ | 30-40 | 60-80 | | 1965-1993 |
| 2045 | Basset Hound | 5 | 30-40 | 60-80 | | 1965-1993 |

| Model No | Name of Model | Height inches | Current Value £ | US$ | DA No | Production Period |
|---|---|---|---|---|---|---|
| 2107A | King Charles Spaniel 'Blenheim' – brown/white | 5¼ | 30-40 | 60-80 | | 1967-1993 |
| 2107B | King Charles Spaniel 'Josephine of Blagreaves' – black, brown & white | 5¼ | 40-60 | 80-120 | | 1967-1993 |
| 2108 | Poodle 'Ivanola Gold Digger' in black or white | 5¾ | 125-175 | 250-350 | | 1967-1971 |
| ****2109 | Jack Russel Terrier | 2⅝ | 12·95 | RRP | | 1967-C |
| ****2112 | Cairn Terrier | 2¾ | 15-20 | 30-40 | | 1967-1995 |
| ***2221 | St Bernard 'Corna Garth Stroller' | 5¾ | 40-60 | 80-120 | | 1968-1988 |
| 2232 | Old English Sheep Dog | 11½ | 60-75 | 120-150 | 84 | 1968-1994 |
| ****2262 | Foxhound (see 944) | 2½ | 9·95 | RRP | | 1969-C |
| ****2263 | Foxhound (see 941) | 2⅞ | 9·95 | RRP | | 1969-C |
| ****2264 | Foxhound (see 943) | 2⅞ | 9·95 | RRP | | 1969-C |
| ****2265 | Foxhound (see 942) | 2¾ | 9·95 | RRP | | 1969-C |
| 2271 | Dalmatian sitting | 13¾ | 100-125 | 200-250 | 85 | 1969-1996 |
| 2285 | Afghan Hound 'Hajubah of Davlen' | 5½ | 30-40 | 60-80 | | 1969-1993 |
| øø2286 | Dachshund | 10½ | 75-100 | 150-200 | | 1969-1982 |
| 2287 | Golden Retriever 'Cabus Cadet' | 5¾ | 30-40 | 60-80 | | 1969-1993 |
| 2299 | Doberman Pinscher 'Annastock Lance' | 5¾ | 30-40 | 60-80 | | 1970-1993 |
| 2300 | Beagle sitting | 12¾ | 125-150 | 250-300 | | 1969-1982 |
| 2314 | Labrador | 13½ | 100-125 | | 86 | 1970-1996 |
| 2339 | Poodle (black or white) | 5¾ | 40-60 | 80-120 | | 1970-1982 |
| 2377 | Yorkshire Terrier | 10¼ | 75-100 | 150-200 | 87 | 1971-1994 |
| 2410 | Alsatian | 14 | 100-125 | | 88 | 1972-1996 |
| ****2448 | Lakeland Terrier | 3¼ | 9·95 | RRP | | 1975-C |
| ****2454 | Chihuahua (on cushion) | 2⅞ | 11·50 | RRP | | 1975-C |
| 2929 | Collie Head (on wood mount) | 5¾ | 25-30 | 50-60 | | 1986-1988 |
| 2932 | Alsatian Head (on wood mount) | 5¾ | 25-30 | 50-60 | | 1986-1988 |
| *2946 | Meal Time | 3½ | 30-40 | 60-80 | | 1987-1988 |
| *2947 | Gnawing | 4¼ | 30-40 | 60-80 | | 1987-1988 |
| *2948 | Play Time | 3¾ | 30-40 | 60-80 | | 1987-1988 |
| *2949 | Juggling | 3 | 30-40 | 60-80 | | 1987-1988 |
| *2950 | Nap Time | 4½ | 30-40 | 60-80 | | 1987-1988 |
| *2951 | Caught It | 2¾ | 30-40 | 60-80 | | 1987-1988 |
| 2979 | Pointer on base (gloss) | 6½ | 75-100 | 150-200 | | 1986-1987 |
| 2980 | Cocker Spaniel on base (matt only) (Golden or Orange & White) | 8¼ | 40-60 | 80-120 | 108 | 1986-1995 |
| øøø2982 | Pekinese | 5½ | 20-25 | 40-50 | 113 | 1986-1995 |
| øøø2984 | Norfolk Terrier | 4 | 20-25 | 40-50 | 114 | 1986-1995 |
| øøø2985 | Poodle on cushion | 5 | 40-60 | 80-120 | 115 | 1986-1995 |
| 2986 | English Setter on base (matt only) Gordon | 8½ | 40-60 | 80-120 | 109 | 1986-1995 |
| 3011 | English Pointer on base (matt only) | 7'¾ | 40-60 | 80-120 | 110 | 1986-1995 |
| øøø3013 | Dachshund | 4½ | 20-25 | 40-50 | 116 | 1986-1995 |
| øøø3055 | Rottweiler | 5½ | 32·95 | RRP | 99 | 1988-C |
| øøø3058 | Old English Sheepdog | 5½ | 32·95 | RRP | 100 | 1988-C |
| øøø3060 | Staffordshire Bull Terrier (brindle) | 4 | 32·95 | RRP | 101 | 1988-C |
| 3062 | Labrador on base (matt only) (golden or black) | 6½ | 40-60 | 80-120 | 111 | 1988-1995 |
| 3066 | Retriever on base (matt only) (golden) | 7½ | 40-60 | 80-120 | 112 | 1988-1995 |

| Model No | Name of Model | Height inches | Current Value £ | US$ | DA No | Production Period |
|---|---|---|---|---|---|---|
| øøø3070 | Afghan Hound | $5\frac{1}{2}$ | 30-40 | 60-80 | 102 | 1988-1996 |
| øøø3073 | Alsatian | $5\frac{3}{4}$ | 32·95 | RRP | 103 | 1988-C |
| øøø3080 | Shetland Sheepdog | 5 | 30-40 | 60-80 | 117 | 1988-1995 |
| øøø3081 | Boxer | $5\frac{1}{2}$ | 32·95 | RRP | 104 | 1988-C |
| øøø3082 | Cairn Terrier | $4\frac{1}{2}$ | 30-40 | 60-80 | 118 | 1988-1995 |
| øøø3083 | Yorkshire Terrier | 5 | 30-40 | 60-80 | 119 | 1988-1995 |
| øøø3121 | Doberman | $5\frac{1}{4}$ | 30-40 | 60-80 | 105 | 1989-1996 |
| øøø3129 | Rough Collie | $5\frac{1}{2}$ | 30-40 | 60-80 | 106 | 1989-1996 |
| øøø3135 | Springer Spaniel | 5 | 32·95 | RRP | 107 | 1989-C |
| 3149 | West Highland Terrier white | 5 | 20-25 | 40-50 | 120 | 1989-1995 |
| 3155 | Cavalier King Charles Spaniel | 5 | 30-40 | 60-80 | 121 | 1989-1995 |
| 3258 | Alsatian | $3\frac{1}{4}$ | 12·95 | RRP | | 1991-C |
| 3260 | Rottweiler | $3\frac{1}{4}$ | 12·95 | RRP | | 1991-C |
| 3262 | Yorkshire Terrier | $3\frac{1}{4}$ | 9·95 | RRP | | 1991-C |
| 3270 | Golden Retriever | 3 | 9·95 | RRP | | 1991-C |
| 3375 | Pair of Hounds | $2\frac{1}{2}$ | 12·95 | RRP | | 1993-C |
| 3376 | Pair of Golden Retrievers | 2 | 12·95 | RRP | | 1993-C |
| 3377 | Cocker Spaniel | 3 | 9·95 | RRP | | 1993-C |
| 3378 | Alsatian | $2\frac{1}{2}$ | 9·95 | RRP | | 1993-C |
| 3379 | Bulldog | $2\frac{1}{2}$ | 9·95 | RRP | | 1993-C |
| 3380 | Jack Russell | $2\frac{1}{2}$ | 9·95 | RRP | | 1993-C |
| 3381 | Retriever | 2 | 9·95 | RRP | | 1993-C |
| 3382 | Scottish Terrier | 3 | 9·95 | RRP | | 1993-C |
| 3383 | Pair of Cocker Spaniels | 2 | 12·95 | RRP | | 1993-C |
| 3384 | Pair of Bulldogs | $2\frac{1}{4}$ | 9·95 | RRP | | 1994-C |
| 3385 | Dalmatian | 3 | 14·95 | RRP | | 1994-C |
| 3436 | Cavalier King Charles Spaniel | $2\frac{1}{2}$ | 9·95 | RRP | | 1994-C |
| 3467 | Pair of West Highland White Terriers | 2 | 9·95 | RRP | | 1994-C |
| 3468 | Pair of Old English Sheepdogs | 2 | 12·95 | RRP | | 1995-C |
| 3475 | Pair of Boxers | $2\frac{1}{4}$ | 14·95 | RRP | | 1995-C |
| 3490 | Pair of Rottweilers | 2 | 14·95 | RRP | | 1995-C |

*Note: The 24 dogs numbered between 2979 and 3155 can be found either with the Doulton or Beswick mark but the Beswick mark will command a higher price.*

*\*These six dogs were taken out of the Doulton Character Dog HN range (nos 1158, 1159, 2654, 1103, 1099 and 1097) and given Beswick numbers.*
*\*\*Re-modelled 1969 with thinner tail and legs and renumbered*
*\*\*\*Available in matt 1970-1989*
*\*\*\*\*Available in matt 1984-1989*
*øFound in at least 6 different colourways*
*øøAvailable in tan or black & tan*
*øøøAvailable in matt until 1989*
*†Available in left and right hand versions and currently sold in pairs*
*††Available in golden, black, liver & white or black & white*
*†††Also available as a money box*
*≠ Prices are per pair*

# Farm Animals

(All current farm animals carry the Beswick backstamp)

In order to maintain their reputation for realistic images of animals, authentic in every detail, Beswick designers have literally been 'down on the farm' for inspiration. Modellers have spent days in the field getting to know the subjects of their study in order to produce an accurate model which is a faithful representation of a champion breed. Many of the models actually carry the name of the award winning animal which inspired the artists. This is particularly true of the cattle and pigs which were modelled by Arthur Gredington. Introduced from 1952 onwards these are still very popular today, particularly among farming communities.

In recent years the champion breeds have been modelled by Graham Tongue and he recalls that the Charolais Bull which posed for his Connoisseur model in 1973 was the largest he had ever seen.

The recent pedigree bulls contrast dramatically with Beswick's first farm animal: a delightful lamb in playful mood modelled by Miss Greaves (323). This light-hearted approach can also be traced throughout the history of Beswick animals and was revived in the Farmyard Humour collection which included a snoozing piglet on the back of the mother pig (2746) and a modern version of the traditional Staffordshire cow-creamer, Daisy the Cow (2792) both now withdrawn. These can be found in the 'Comical Animals and Birds' section.

In 1992, Beswick Collectors Circle members were able to purchase a 'red' and white Friesian bull, cow and a lying calf (2690 of the Connoisseur set) in a very limited edition of just 130 sets. These were finished in gloss and are now much sought after. It is possible that a few matt pieces were also done at the same time.

| Model No | Name of Model | Size inches | Current Value £ | US$ | Production Period |
|---|---|---|---|---|---|
| 323 | Lamb on base | 8 | 75-100 | 150-200 | 1934-1954 |
| 369 | Donkey on base | 8 | 75-100 | 150-200 | 1936-1954 |
| 398 | Goat | 4½ | 40-50 | 80-100 | 1936-1954 |
| 832 | Pig | 3¾ | 30-35 | 60-70 | 1940-1971 |
| 833 | Piglet | 1¾ | 15-20 | 30-40 | 1940-1971 |
| 834 | Piglet | 1½ | 15-20 | 30-40 | 1940-1971 |
| 854 | Hereford Calf | 4¾ | 50-75 | 100-140 | 1940-1961 |
| 897 | Donkey Foal (deferred see 950) | 5¾ | 50-75 | 100-140 | 1941 only |
| 899 | Cow (deferred see 948) | 5 | 150-175 | 300-350 | 1941 only |
| *901 | Hereford Calf | 4 | 50-75 | 100-150 | 1941-1967 |
| 935 | Sheep | 3½ | 20-25 | 40-50 | 1941-1971 |
| 936 | Lamb | 3¼ | 15-20 | 30-40 | 1941-1971 |
| 937 | Lamb | 2 | 10-15 | 20-30 | 1941-1971 |
| 938 | Lamb | 2 | 10-15 | 20-30 | 1941-1971 |
| 948 | Hereford Cow | 5 | 150-175 | 300-350 | 1944-1957 |
| 949 | Hereford Bull | 5¾ | 150-175 | 300-350 | 1944-1957 |
| 950 | Donkey Foal | 5¾ | 50-75 | 100-140 | 1944-1957 |
| 1035 | Goat | 5½ | 75-100 | 150-200 | 1945-1970 |
| 1036 | Kid | 2½ | 40-50 | 80-100 | 1945-1970 |
| 1248 | Guernsey Cow (Horns separate) | 4¼ | 75-100 | 150-200 | 1952-1975 |

| Model No | Name of Model | Size inches | Current Value £ | US$ | Production Period |
|---|---|---|---|---|---|
| **1248 | Guernsey Cow (Horns moulded) | 4¼ | 60-80 | 120-160 | 1975-1990 |
| ***1249 | Jersey Calf | 2¾ | 14·95 | RRP | 1954-C |
| ***1249 | Friesian Calf | 2¾ | 14·95 | RRP | 1954-C |
| ***1249 | Ayrshire Calf | 2 ¾ | 30-40 | 60-80 | 1954-1990 |
| ***1249 | Guernsey Calf | 2¾ | 30-40 | 60-80 | 1952-1990 |
| 1249 | Hereford Calf | 2¾ | 40-50 | 50-60 | 1992-1993 |
| ***1249 | Aberdeen Angus Calf | 2¾ | 40-50 | 80-100 | 1975-1985 |
| **1345 | Jersey Cow – 'Newton Tinkle' | 4¼ | 29·95 | RRP | 1954-C |
| **1350 | Ayrshire Cow 'Ickham Bessie' | 5 | 75-100 | 150-200 | 1954-1990 |
| **1360 | Hereford Cow | 4¼ | 29·95 | RRP | 1954-C |
| **1362 | Friesian Cow 'Claybury Leegwater' | 4½ | 29·95 | RRP | 1954-C |
| **1362 | Friesian Cow (red) | 4½ | 300-350 | 600-700 | 1992 only |
| **1363 | Hereford Bull | 4½ | 29·95 | RRP | 1955-C |
| +øø1364 | Donkey | 4½ | 16·95 | RRP | 1955-C |
| 1406 | Dairy Shorthorn Calf | 3 | 100-125 | 200-250 | 1957-1973 |
| 1406 | Hereford Calf | 3 | 75-100 | 150-200 | 1956-1975 |
| 1406 | Aberdeen Angus Calf | 3 | 75-100 | 150-200 | 1958-1975 |
| 1410 | Cow (CM series) | 7⅛ | 150-200 | 300-400 | 1956-1961 |
| **1422 | Jersey Bull 'Dunsley Coy Boy' | 4½ | 29·95 | RRP | 1956-C |
| **1439 | Friesian Bull 'Coddington Hilt Bar' | 4¾ | 34·95 | RRP | 1956-C |
| **1439 | Friesian Bull (red) | 4¾ | 300-350 | 600-700 | 1992 only |
| **1451 | Guernsey Bull 'Sabrina's Sir Richmond 14th' | 4¾ | 60-80 | 120-160 | 1956-1990 |
| øø1452 | White Sow 'Champion Wallqueen 40th' | 2¾ | 16·95 | RRP | 1956-C |
| øø1453 | White Boar 'Wall Champion Boy 53rd' | 2¾ | 16·95 | RRP | 1956-C |
| **1454 | Ayrshire Bull 'Whitehill Mandate' | 5¼ | 75-100 | 150-200 | 1956-1990 |
| 1473 | Pig (CM series) | 2½ | 125-150 | 250-300 | 1957-1966 |
| 1504 | Dairy Shorthorn Bull 'Gwersylt Lord Oxford 74th' | 5 | 300-400 | 600-800 | 1957-1973 |
| 1510 | Dairy Shorthorn Cow 'Eaton Wild Eyes 91st' | 4¾ | 300-400 | 600-800 | 1957-1973 |
| 1511 | Sow 'Merrywood Silver Wings 56th' Saddleback | 2¾ | 150-200 | 300-400 | 1957-1969 |
| 1512 | Boar 'Far Acre Viscount 3rd' Saddleback | 2¾ | 150-200 | 300-400 | 1957-1969 |
| ø**1562 | Aberdeen Angus Bull | 4½ | 75-100 | 150-200 | 1958-1990 |
| ø**1563 | Aberdeen Angus Cow | 4¼ | 75-100 | 150-200 | 1959-1990 |
| **1740 | Highland Cow | 5½ | 75-100 | 150-200 | 1961-1990 |
| 1746 | Galloway Bull 'Silver Dunn' | 4½ | 500-600 | 1000-1200 | 1961-1968 |
| 1746 | Galloway Bull — belted | 4½ | 500-600 | 1300-1500 | 1963-1968 |
| 1746 | Galloway Bull (black) | 4½ | 500-600 | 1000-1250 | 1961-1968 |
| øø1765 | Black Faced Sheep | 3¼ | 13·95 | RRP | 1961-C |
| ***1827 | Highland Calf | 3 | 30-40 | 60-80 | 1962-1990 |
| ***1827 | Hereford Calf | 3 | 14·95 | RRP | 1985-C |
| ***1827 | Aberdeen Angus Calf | 3 | 40-60 | 80-120 | 1985-1990 |
| ***1827 | Charolais Calf | 3 | 14·95 | RRP | 1985-C |
| øø1828 | Black Faced Lamb | 2⅜ | 7·95 | RRP | 1962-C |
| 1917 | Merino Ram | 4½ | 250-300 | 550-625 | 1963-1966 |
| **2008 | Highland Bull | 5 | 75-100 | 150-200 | 1965-1990 |
| øø2110 | Donkey Foal | 4⅜ | 13·95 | RRP | 1967-C |
| øø2267 | Donkey | 5½ | 19·95 | RRP | 1969-C |
| **2463 | Charolais Bull (small) | 5 | 34·95 | RRP | 1975-C |
| **2549 | Polled Hereford Bull | 5 | 59·95 | RRP | 1975-C |
| 2690 | Lying Calf | 2¼ | 100-125 | 200-250 | 1992 only |

| Model | Name of Model | Size | Current Value | | Production |
|---|---|---|---|---|---|
| No | | inches | £ | US$ | Period |
| ****3071 | Black Faced Ram | 3½ | 19·95 | RRP | 1988-C |
| ****3075 | Charolais Cow | 4⅞ | 29·95 | RRP | 1988-C |

*Early versions have an open mouth
**Available in matt finish 1985-1989
***Available in matt finish 1987-1989
****Available in matt finish 1989 only
øSome are backstamped 'Approved by Aberdeen Angus Cattle Society'
øøAvailable in matt finish 1984-1989
+Early version has gap between tail and hind legs and the ears are upright, not forward

# Fish

(All models carry the Beswick mark)

The sport of many is to sit in quiet solitude on the bank of an equally quiet river and hope that one's knowledge and skill will land a good catch. Any one of the excellent range of fish portrayed by Beswick would be an appropriate addition to the angler's collection.

Fish studies would appear to have been a new departure for Beswick, although an old catalogue contains an illustration of a dolphin jug.

All the models are supported on a base, some balanced on their tail whilst others lie horizontally. Often the fins and tail are vulnerable to damage and it is therefore difficult to find perfect examples.

As with all Beswick animal studies, a team of experts visited Beswick to verify the accuracy of each fish model. Not only were they concerned to check the size and proportions of the fish, but as Colin Melbourne remembers, the number of scales were actually counted!

| Model | Name of Model | Size | Current Value | | Production |
|---|---|---|---|---|---|
| No | | inches | £ | US$ | Period |
| 1032 | Trout | 6¼ | 100-150 | 200-300 | 1945-1975 |
| 1047 | Angel Fish | 7¼ | 200-250 | 400-500 | 1946-1966 |
| 1232 | Oceanic Bonito | 7¼ | 200-250 | 400-500 | 1952-1967 |
| 1233 | Atlantic Salmon | 6½ | 200-250 | 400-500 | 1952-1969 |
| 1235 | Barracuda | 4¾ | 200-250 | 400-500 | 1952-1967 |
| 1243 | Marlin | 5½ | 300-350 | 600-700 | 1952-1969 |
| 1246 | Golden Trout | 6 | 100-150 | 175-200 | 1952-1969 |
| 1266 | Large Mouthed Black Bass | 5 | 200-250 | 400-500 | 1952-1967 |
| 1390 | Trout (small) | 4 | 75-100 | 150-200 | 1955-1975 |
| 1485 | Black Bass | 6 | 200-250 | 400-500 | 1957-1967 |
| 1599 | Trout ash bowl | 5 | 75-100 | 150-200 | 1959-1970 |
| 1874 | Roach | 4¼ | 100-150 | 200-300 | 1963-1970 |
| 1875 | Perch | 4¼ | 100-150 | 200-300 | 1963-1970 |
| 2066 | Salmon | 8 | 150-200 | 300-400 | 1966-1975 |
| 2087 | Trout | 6 | 100-150 | 200-300 | 1966-1975 |
| *2254 | Fish ('Moda' range) | 4⅝ | 50-60 | 100-120 | 1968-1970 |

*Matt finish

# Horses, Foals and Ponies

(All current items in this section produced since August 1989, carry a Royal Doulton backstamp)

This is the subject for which Beswick is best known and it is the largest section of all with over 150 recorded models, 22 being continuously in production for over 35 years. The first horse (701), modelled by Arthur Gredington in 1939, was based on Bois Russell the winner of the 1938 Derby. It was innovatory as it introduced the concept of modelling from champions and named breeds. *The Pottery Gazette and Glass Trade Review* was quick to praise and appreciate John Beswick's new style. In April 1942 it wrote: ". . . among Beswick's wares were a host of splendidly modelled and lifelike animal subjects including some particularly fine horses and foals — both hunters and shires, this being a type of potting for which the firm has established a big reputation . . ."

Since Bois Russell, many famous racehorses have been immortalised by Beswick; Arkle, Grundy, Red Rum, Troy, Nijinski and Cardigan Bay being just some of the well known names among them. Until 1983 collectors could opt to have the horses ridden by equally famous jockeys such as Lester Pigott on Nijinski.

It has always been something of a gamble for the Beswick modellers to choose a horse which will continue to be as successful in the future as it has been in the past. The horse's owner is contacted and, once permission for the model is obtained, the modeller and design manager arrange a visit to study the animal. During the visit they meet and talk to all who are connected with the horse — the owner, the trainer and the grooms so that its personality can be fully understood. The horse is studied from all angles, particularly when it is at its most relaxed, paying particular attention to the pose, facial expressions, marks and, above all, its character. Sketches are made and photographs are taken to check that markings, colours and other details are accurate. Although all horses have a similar bone and muscle structure the expression and character of each is different and it is this which the modeller wishes to portray in clay. Back in the studio, the modeller starts working with the clay to put this into effect. The bone measurements and pose are positioned first and over this the rib cage and muscle structure are built up with sinews, veins, hair and mane following. In this way the physical appearance as well as the character and spirit of each horse is captured.

Throughout his work the sculptor has had to bear in mind the size of the finished model, the various methods of production, the type of decoration and the eventual price. The size is of particular importance since shrinkage of one twelfth occurs during firing. Consultations between the modeller and designer are frequent. The completed model is checked against the photographs and then the owner is invited to the factory to comment on its fidelity. One or two minor alterations are usually made as a result, and the finished, fully approved model then passes to the mould maker.

An early series of horses portrayed Mountain and Moorland ponies. In producing these, Beswick worked closely with R. S. Summerhays, a past President of the National Pony Society, who approved each model for accuracy of shape and colour. He also wrote an introduction with comments on each breed of pony for the accompanying sales brochure of the period.

Not all of Beswick's horses are based on named animals, but all must have the correct proportions and anatomical structure to maintain Beswick's high standards. Once these considerations are fulfilled, endless variations are possible.

Since 1981 Graham Tongue has romanticised the character of the horse in the 'Spirit' collection, with evocative names such as 'Spirit of Fire', 'Spirit of Freedom' and 'Spirit of Earth', the latter portraying a massive working horse. Clydesdales, Shires and Percherons have all featured in the collection over the years, some complete with leather harness.

Originally the racehorse (1564) was also available with a detachable leather saddle. The first model to actually include a rider was the Huntsman (868), which is now withdrawn. Since then a Cowboy, an Indian, a Bedouin Arab, a Canadian Mountie, a Lifeguard and a Guardsman have all appeared on horseback. The Guardsman was modelled at Kensington Barracks and it took over two hours to model the details of his uniform alone. Equally faithful in every detail are the portraits of Her Majesty, Queen Elizabeth II on Imperial, and his Royal Highness, the Duke of Edinburgh on Alamein.

To mark the Beswick Centenary in 1994, it was decided to model 'Cancara', the black horse, a Trakehner stallion. Available with a Beswick backstamp during 1994 only, thereafter it carries a Royal Doulton backstamp.

With such a variety of colours used for decorating horses over the years, it is impossible here, to give all the relevant information which is needed. I suggest that you obtain a copy of Marilyn Sweets book *A Guide to Horses, Ponies & Foals* where you will find all the detail required. In the following lists, the current value given is for the 'basic' brown horse and makes no allowance for special colours. Any colour, other than brown, will command a higher price.

A model, well worth mentioning here, is 'Kruger' a Welsh Mountain Pony, the last working pit pony at the Chatterley Whitfield mine when he retired in 1931. In 1987, following the mines earlier closure, a mining museum was set up on the site and it was suggested that a model of him should be made and presented to Princess Anne, when she opened the museum on 13th October, 1987. A total of 4 were cast, one to the Princess, one to the mining museum, one to the Beswick museum and the fourth was auctioned for charity.

Financial difficulties forced closure of the mining museum in 1994 and the model was offered at auction. The price realised was nearly £2600 / US$5000 and this Beswick model is therefore the most valuable ever. The model was based upon Beswick Connoisseur No 2541, a Welsh Mountain Pony, and Graham Tongue, chief designer of the John Beswick Studio of Royal Doulton, recalls that he only had about two weeks in which to prepare a new model. The other interesting thing is that this is the first piece since 1934 not to be allocated a shape number.

The discontinued colours, referred to in the following lists are: Chestnut (dark), Blue (Turquoise), Grey (Heavy Dapple), Painted white body (eyes and feet black), Opaque (all-over white), Chestnut (Red-brown), Dapple Grey (light), Black or white, matt colours also from 1970.

# Horses

| Model No | Name of Model | Size inches | Current Value £ | US$ | DA Number | Production Period |
|---|---|---|---|---|---|---|
| **701 | 'Bois Roussel' Derby Winner 1938 | 8 | 29·95 | RRP | 42 | 1939-C |
| 701 | Up to 10 discontinued colours | | 30-700 | 60-1400 | | |
| 855 | Horse | 6 | 29·95 | RRP | 44 | 1940-C |
| 855 | Up to 7 discontinued colours | | 40-500 | 80-1000 | | |
| **976 | Mare | 6¾ | 29·95 | RRP | 46 | 1942-C |
| 976 | Up to 8 discontinued colours | | 40-500 | 80-1000 | | |
| 976 | Mare (dun gloss) Collectors Special | 6¾ | 50 | 100 | | 1997 only |
| **1182 | Horse | 8¾ | 34·95 | RRP | 48 | 1950-C |
| 1182 | Up to 10 discontinued colours | | 40-500 | 80-1000 | | |
| **1261 | Palomino | 6¾ | 29·95 | RRP | 49 | 1952-C |
| 1261 | Up to 10 discontinued colours | | 40-500 | 80-1000 | | |
| 1265 | Arab Xayal | 6¼ | 29·95 | RRP | 50 | 1952-C |
| 1265 | Up to 7 discontinued colours | | 40-500 | 80-1000 | | |
| 1361 | Hackney Horse | 7¾ | 80-100 | 160-200 | | 1954-1982 |
| 1361 | Up to 9 discontinued colours | | 100-500 | 200-1000 | | |
| 1373/1 | Pinto Horse (tail hanging loose) | 6½ | 125-150 | 150-300 | | 1955-1982 |
| 1373/2 | Pinto Horse (tail attached to leg) | 6½ | 100-125 | 200-250 | | 1982-1990 |
| 1373 | Up to 5 discontinued colours | | 150-250 | 300-500 | | |
| 1411 | Horse (C.M. series) | 8¾ | 200-250 | 400-500 | | 1956-1971 |
| 1484 | Hunter Horse (as 1501) | 6¾ | 75-100 | 150-200 | | 1957-1982 |
| 1484 | Up to 7 discontinued colours | | 100-500 | 200-1000 | | |
| 1516 | Appaloosa | 5¼ | 300-400 | 600-800 | | 1957-1966 |
| 1516 | Up to 6 discontinued colours | | 300-700 | 600-1400 | | |
| 1549 | Horse | 7½ | 29·95 | RRP | 51 | 1958-C |
| 1549 | Up to 9 discontinued colours | | 40-500 | 80-1000 | | |
| 1557 | 'Imperial' (modified 1546) | 8¼ | 75-100 | 150-200 | | 1958-1982 |
| 1557 | Up to 7 discontinued colours | | 100-500 | 200-1000 | | |
| 1564 | Racehorse with or without saddle | 11¼ | 80-100 | 160-200 | | 1959-1980 |
| 1564 | Up to 6 discontinued colours | | 100-500 | 200-1000 | | |
| 1734 | Hunter Horse | 11¼ | 80-100 | 160-200 | | 1961-1983 |
| 1734 | Up to 6 discontinued colours | | 100-500 | 200-1000 | | |
| **1771 | Arab Horse | 7½ | 29·95 | RRP | 52 | 1961-C |
| 1771 | Up to 10 discontinued colours | | 40-500 | 80-1000 | | |
| 1772 | Thoroughbred Horse | 8 | 29·95 | RRP | 53 | 1961-C |
| 1772 | Up to 8 discontinued colours | | 40-500 | 80-1000 | | |
| 1772A | Appaloosa | 8 | 52·50 | RRP | 68 | 1961-C |
| 1793 | Welsh Cob | 7½ | 125-150 | 250-300 | | 1962-1982 |
| 1793 | Up to 6 discontinued colours | | 150-300 | 300-600 | | |
| 1812 | Mare | 5¾ | 75-100 | 150-200 | | 1962-1990 |
| 1812 | Up to 10 discontinued colours | | 100-300 | 200-600 | | |
| 1991 | Mare | 5½ | 23·95 | RRP | 55 | 1964-C |
| 1991 | Up to 9 discontinued colours | | 50-400 | 100-800 | | |
| **1992 | Stallion | 5½ | 21·95 | RRP | 56 | 1964-C |
| 1992 | Up to 9 discontinued colours | | 50-400 | 100-800 | | |
| 2186 | Quarter Horse | 8¼ | 50-60 | 100-120 | | 1968-1982 |
| 2282 | Norwegian Fjord Horse | 6¼ | 250-300 | 500-600 | | 1969-1975 |
| 2421 | The Winner Racehorse | 9¾ | 50-60 | 100-120 | | 1972-1982 |
| 2421 | Up to 2 discontinued colours | | 60-100 | 120-200 | | |
| 2459 | Mare lying (Shire) | 5 | 300-400 | 600-800 | | 1973-1976 |
| †2466 | 'Black Beauty' Horse | 7⅛ | 44·95 | RRP | 65 | 1973-C |
| 2671 | 'Moonlight' White Racehorse | 11¼ | 75-100 | 150-200 | 35 | 1980-1996 |
| 2671 | 'Sunburst' Palomino | 11¼ | 75-100 | 150-200 | 36 | 1986-1995 |

| Model No | Name of Model | Size inches | Current Value £ | US$ | DA Number | Production Period |
|---|---|---|---|---|---|---|
| 2671 | 'Nightshade' Black horse | 11¼ | 75-100 | 150-200 | | 1986-1989 |
| 2671 | Up to 2 discontinued colours | | 75-100 | 150-200 | | |
| **2688 | 'Spirit of the Wind' with or without wood base | 8 | 49·95 | RRP | 57 | 1980-C |
| 2688 | Up to 8 discontinued colours | | 40-60 | 80-120 | | |
| **2689 | 'Spirit of Freedom' | 7 | 49·95 | RRP | 58 | 1980-C |
| 2689 | Up to 7 discontinued colours | | 40-60 | 80-120 | | |
| 2703 | 'Spirit of Youth' (as 2466) | 6½ | 44·95 | RRP | 59 | 1981-C |
| †2703 | 'Spirit of Youth' (on base) | 7⅛ | 49·95 | RRP | | 1981-C |
| 2703 | Up to 7 discontinued colours | | 50-75 | 100-150 | | |
| **2829 | 'Spirit of Fire' | 8 | 30-50 | 60-125 | 60 | 1983-1994 |
| 2829 | Up to 7 discontinued colours | | 40-60 | 80-120 | | |
| †2916 | 'Spirit of Peace' lying | 5 | 40-60 | 80-120 | 63 | 1985-1996 |
| 2916 | Up to 7 discontinued colours | | 50-60 | 100-120 | | |

# Foals

| Model No | Name of Model | Size inches | Current Value £ | US$ | DA Number | Production Period |
|---|---|---|---|---|---|---|
| 728 | Foal | 5 | 30-40 | 60-80 | | 1939-1971 |
| 728 | Up to 11 discontinued colours | | 30-500 | 60-1000 | | |
| 763 | Foal (re-modelled 1956) | 3¼ | 30-40 | 60-80 | | 1939-1976 |
| 763 | Up to 8 discontinued colours | | 30–500 | 60-1000 | | |
| **815 | Foal | 3¼ | 12·50 | RRP | 74 | 1940-C |
| 815 | Up to 11 discontinued colours | | 10-400 | 20-800 | | |
| 836 | Foal (re-modelled 1958) | 5 | 30-40 | 60-80 | | 1940-1982 |
| 836 | Up to 9 discontinued colours | | 30-500 | 60-1000 | | |
| **915 | Foal lying | 3¼ | 12·50 | RRP | 75 | 1941-C |
| 915 | Up to 8 discontinued colours | | 30-500 | 60-1000 | | |
| **946 | Foal | 3¼ | 12·50 | RRP | 76 | 1941-C |
| 946 | Up to 9 discontinued colours | | 10-400 | 20-800 | | |
| **947 | Foal | 4½ | 14·95 | RRP | 77 | 1941-C |
| 947 | Up to 9 discontinued colours | | 10-400 | 20-800 | | |
| 947 | Foal (dun gloss) Collectors Special | 4½ | 25 | 50 | | 1997 only |
| 951 | Foal (Shire) | 6¼ | 20-30 | 40-60 | | 1941-1971 |
| 951 | Up to 7 discontinued colours | | 30-500 | 60-1000 | | |
| 996 | Foal | 3¼ | 10-15 | 20-30 | | 1943-1976 |
| 996 | Up to 8 discontinued colours | | 30-300 | 60-600 | | |
| 997 | Foal | 3¼ | 12·50 | RRP | 78 | 1943-C |
| 997 | Up to 8 discontinued colours | | 30-300 | 60-600 | | |
| 1034 | Shetland Foal | 3¾ | 12·50 | RRP | 79 | 1945-C |
| 1034 | Up to 3 discontinued colours | | 30-40 | 60-80 | | |
| 1053 | Foal (Shire) | 5 | 30-40 | 60-80 | | 1946-1982 |
| 1053 | Up to 9 discontinued colours | | 30-500 | 60-1000 | | |
| 1084 | Foal | 4½ | 30-40 | 60-80 | | 1947-1982 |
| 1084 | Up to 9 discontinued colours | | 30-500 | 60-1000 | | |
| 1085 | Foal | 3½ | 30-40 | 60-80 | | 1947-1971 |
| 1085 | Up to 8 discontinued colours | | 30-400 | 600-800 | | |
| 1407 | Foal | 4½ | 12·50 | RRP | 80 | 1956-C |
| 1407 | Up to 9 discontinued colours | | 30-500 | 60-1000 | | |
| 1813 | Foal | 4½ | 12·50 | RRP | 81 | 1962-C |
| 1813 | Up to 8 discontinued colours | | 30-150 | 60-300 | | |
| 1816 | Foal | 3⅜ | 12·50 | RRP | 82 | 1962-C |
| 1816 | Up to 6 discontinued colours | | 30-150 | 60-300 | | |
| 1817 | Foal | 3¼ | 15-20 | 30-40 | | 1962-1975 |
| 1817 | Up to 6 discontinued colours | | 30-150 | 60-300 | | |
| 2460 | Foal (Shire) – lying | 3½ | 100-125 | 200-250 | | 1973-1976 |
| †2536 | 'Black Beauty' Foal | 5⅞ | 21·95 | RRP | 66 | 1975-C |

| Model No | Name of Model | Size inches | Current Value £ | US$ | DA Number | Production Period |
|---|---|---|---|---|---|---|
| 2536 | Up to 4 discontinued colours | | 30-100 | 60-200 | | |
| 2837 | 'Springtime' | 4 | 21·95 | RRP | 69 | 1983-C |
| 2837 | 'Springtime' (on base) | 4½ | 23·95 | RRP | | 1983-C |
| 2837 | Up to 3 discontinued colours | | 30-40 | 60-80 | | |
| 2839 | 'Young Spirit' | 4 | 15-20 | 30-40 | 70 | 1983-1996 |
| 2839 | 'Young Spirit' (on base) | 4½ | 20-25 | 40-50 | | 1983-1996 |
| 2839 | Up to 3 discontinued colours | | 30-40 | 60-80 | | |
| 2875 | 'Sunlight' | 4 | 15-20 | 30-40 | 71 | 1983-1996 |
| 2875 | 'Sunlight' (on base) | 4½ | 20-25 | 40-50 | | 1985-1996 |
| 2875 | Up to 3 discontinued colours | | 30-40 | 60-80 | | |
| 2876 | 'Adventure' | 4 | 18·95 | RRP | 72 | 1983-C |
| 2876 | 'Adventure' (on base) | 4½ | 23·95 | RRP | | 1985-C |
| 2876 | Up to 3 discontinued colours | | 30-40 | 60-80 | | |
| øø– | Dartmoor Foal – lying | | | | | 1998- |

# Horses on Base

| Model No | Name of Model | Size inches | Current Value £ | US$ | DA Number | Production Period |
|---|---|---|---|---|---|---|
| 766 | Foal (on or off base) | 3¾ | 100-400 | 200-800 | | 1939-1954 |
| 953 | Mare & Foal | 7¾ | 100-150 | 200-300 | | 1941-1983 |
| 953 | Up to 7 discontinued colours | | 150-500 | 300-1000 | | |
| 1014 | Prancing Horse | 10¼ | 60-80 | 120-160 | | 1945-1990 |
| 1014 | Up to 8 discontinued colours | | 80-500 | 160-1000 | | |
| 1374 | Galloping Palomino | 7½ | 125-150 | 250-300 | | 1955-1975 |
| 1374 | Up to 3 discontinued colours | | 150-500 | 300-1000 | | |
| 1811 | Bay Mare & Foal (in Grey or Brown) | 6 | 100-150 | 200-300 | | 1962-1973 |
| 1918 | Pony ash tray (model 1643) | 11 x 8 | 100-150 | 200-300 | | 1963-1972 |
| 2065 | 'Arkle' Racehorse | 11⅞ | 155·00 | RRP | 15 | 1966-C |
| 2137 | Tang Horse | 8 | 300-400 | 600-800 | | 1967-1972 |
| 2205 | Tang Horse | 13 | 400-500 | 800-1000 | | 1968-1972 |
| 2242 | Arab Horse | 8½ | 300-400 | 600-800 | | 1968-1975 |
| 2269 | Arab Stallion with saddle | 9½ | 500-600 | 1000-1200 | | 1969-1973 |
| 2340 | 'Cardigan Bay'Racehorse | 9¼ | 400-500 | 800-1000 | | 1970-1976 |
| 2345 | 'Nijinsky' Racehorse | 11⅛ | 155·00 | RRP | 16 | 1970-C |
| 2422 | 'Mill Reef' Racehorse | 9 | 100-125 | 200-250 | | 1972-1989 |
| 2431 | Mountie Stallion | 10 | 400-500 | 800-1000 | | 1972-1975 |
| 2510 | 'Red Rum' Racehorse | 12 | 155·00 | RRP | 18 | 1974-C |
| 2540 | 'Psalm' Racehorse | 11½ | 175-200 | 350-400 | | 1975-1982 |
| 2541 | Welsh Mountain Pony | 9 | 200-250 | 400-500 | | 1975-1989 |
| 2558 | 'Grundy' Racehorse | 11¼ | 155·00 | RRP | 20 | 1976-C |
| 2605 | Morgan Horse | 11½ | 100-125 | 200-250 | 28 | 1977-1996 |
| 2608 | 'The Minstrel' Racehorse | 13¼ | 155·00 | RRP | 31 | 1978-C |
| 2674 | 'Troy' Racehorse | 11¾ | 155·00 | RRP | 37 | 1980-C |
| †2688 | 'Spirit of the Wind' | 8 | 49·95 | RRP | 57 | 1980-C |
| †2689 | 'Spirit of Freedom' | 7 | 49·95 | RRP | 58 | 1980-C |
| †2689 & 2536 | 'Spirit of Affection' – Black Beauty Foal & Spirit of Freedom together | 7 | 69·95 | RRP | 64 | 1980-C |
| 2689&2536 | Up to 3 discontinued colours | | 70-100 | 140-200 | | |
| †2703 | 'Spirit of Youth' (same model as 2466) | 7⅛ | 49·95 | RRP | 59 | 1981-C |
| **2829 | 'Spirit of Fire' | 8 | 50-75 | 75-125 | 60 | 1983-1994 |
| †2837 | 'Springtime' (foal) | 4½ | 23·95 | RRP | 69 | 1983-C |
| 2839 | 'Young Spirit' (foal) | 4½ | 15-20 | 30-40 | 70 | 1983-1996 |
| 2875 | 'Sunlight' (foal) | 4½ | 15-20 | 30-40 | 71 | 1983-1996 |
| †2876 | 'Adventure' (foal) | 4½ | 23·95 | RRP | 72 | 1983-C |
| 2914 | 'Spirit of Earth' | 7¾ | 40-60 | 80-120 | 61 | 1985-1993 |
| 2914 | Up to 5 discontinued colours | | 60-90 | 120-190 | | |

| Model No | Name of Model | Size inches | Current Value £ | US$ | DA Number | Production Period |
|---|---|---|---|---|---|---|
| †2916 | 'Spirit of Peace' lying | 5 | 49·95 | RRP | 63 | 1985-C |
| †2935 | 'Spirit of Nature' | 5½ | 40-50 | 80-100 | 73 | 1985-1996 |
| 3021 | Cream Unicorn on china base (very limited issue. Special Commission) | 9¼ | 150-200 | 300-400 | | 1987 only |
| *3426 | 'Cancara' | 15¼ | 275·00 | RRP | 234 | 1994-C |

## Mounted Horses

| Model No | Name of Model | Size inches | Current Value £ | US$ | DA Number | Production Period |
|---|---|---|---|---|---|---|
| 868/1 | Huntsman (Orange coat) on rearing horse, on base (rider leaning back) | 9¾ | 400-500 | 800-1000 | | 1940-1952 |
| 868/2 | Huntsman (Red coat) on rearing horse, on base (rider upright) | 9¼ | 100-125 | 200-250 | | 1952-1994 |
| 868/2 | Up to 7 discontinued colours | | 125-1000 | 250-2000 | | |
| 939 | Girl on horse jumping fence on base (horse as model 982) | 9¾ | 250-300 | 500-600 | | 1941-1962 |
| 982 | Side saddle lady on horse jumping fence on base. (Horse as model 939) | 10 | 250-300 | 500-600 | | 1942-1967 |
| 1037 | Horse & Jockey | 8½ | 250-300 | 500-600 | | 1945-1976 |
| 1145 | 15th Century Knight in armour, mounted on horse | 10¾ | 600-800 | 1200-1600 | | 1949-1969 |
| 1375 | Canadian Mountie | 8¼ | 300-400 | 600-800 | | 1955-1976 |
| 1377 | Mounted Cowboy | 8¾ | 600-800 | 1200-1600 | | 1955-1969 |
| 1391 | Mounted Indian | 8½ | 300-400 | 600-800 | | 1955-1990 |
| 1499 | Girl on Pony | 5½ | 150-200 | 300-400 | | 1957-1976 |
| 1499 | Up to 3 discontinued colours | | 200-700 | 400-1400 | | |
| 1500 | Boy on Pony | 5½ | 150-200 | 300-400 | | 1957-1976 |
| 1500 | Up to 3 discontinued colours | | 200-700 | 400-1400 | | |
| 1501 | Huntsman | 8¼ | 100-125 | 200-250 | | 1957-1994 |
| 1501 | Up to 7 discontinued colours | | 125-1000 | 250-2000 | | |
| 1546 | H.M. Queen Elizabeth II on 'Imperial' | 10½ | 200-250 | 400-500 | | 1958-1980 |
| 1588 | H.R.H. Duke of Edinburgh on 'Alamein' | 10½ | 200-250 | 400-500 | | 1958-1980 |
| 1624 | Mounted Lifeguard of the Household Cavalry | 9½ | 350-450 | 700-900 | | 1959-1977 |
| 1730 | Huntswoman | 8¼ | 100-125 | 200-250 | | 1960-1994 |
| 1730 | Up to 5 discontinued colours | | 125-1000 | 250-2000 | | |
| 1862 | Horse & Jockey (Brown) | 8 | 200-250 | 400-500 | | 1963-1982 |
| 1862 | Horse & Jockey (Grey) | 8 | 225-275 | 450-550 | | 1963-1982 |
| 2084 | 'Arkle' Racehorse on wood base Pat Taaffe up | 12⅝ | 275-325 | 550-650 | | 1966-1980 |
| 2210 | Highwayman on rearing horse (Base set in wood stand) | 13⅞ | 600-800 | 1200-1600 | | 1968-1975 |
| 2275 | Mounted Bedouin Arab (Base set in wood stand) | 11½ | 800-1000 | 1600-2000 | | 1969-1973 |
| 2352 | 'Nijinsky' Racehorse on wood base. Lester Piggott up | 12⅝ | 275-325 | 550-650 | | 1971-1982 |
| 2467 | Lippizzaner with Rider on round or oval base | 10 | 400-500 | 800-1000 | | 1973-1980 |
| 2505 | Steeplechaser on base | 8¾ | 300-350 | 600-700 | | 1974-1980 |
| 2511 | 'Red Rum' Racehorse on wood base B. Fletcher Up | 12¼ | 275-325 | 550-650 | | 1974-1983 |
| 2535 | 'Psalm' Racehorse on wood base Anne Moore Up | 12¾ | 275-325 | 550-650 | | 1975-1982 |
| 2562 | Life-Guard on horseback on wood base | 14½ | 400-450 | 800-900 | 22 | 1976-1996 |

| Model No | Name of Model | Size inches | Current Value £ | US$ | DA Number | Production Period |
|---|---|---|---|---|---|---|
| 2582 | Blues and Royals on horseback on wood base | 14½ | 400-450 | 800-900 | 25 | 1987-1996 |

## Heavy Horses

| Model No | Name of Model | Size inches | Current Value £ | US$ | DA Number | Production Period |
|---|---|---|---|---|---|---|
| 818 | Shire with or without harness | 8½ | 34·95 | RRP | 43 | 1940-C |
| 818 | Up to 11 discontinued colours | | 400-600 | 800-1200 | | |
| 818 | Shire (black) (Collectors Special) | 8½ | 500-600 | 1000-120 | | 1990 only |
| 975 | Trotting Horse (Shire) | 8¾ | 39·95 | RRP | 45 | 1942-C |
| 975 | Up to 8 discontinued colours | | 30-800 | 60-160 | | |
| 975 | Trotting Shire (black) Collectors Special | 8¾ | 100-200 | 200-400 | | 1996 only |
| 1050 | Shire Horse grazing | 5½ | 100-150 | 200-300 | | 1946-1971 |
| 1050 | Up to 6 discontinued colours | | 500-700 | 1000-1400 | | |
| 1359 | 'Hasse Dainty' Suffolk Punch | 8 | 200-300 | 400-600 | | 1954-1971 |
| 2309 | 'Burnham Beauty' (Shire Horse also in working harness) | 10¾ | 60-80 | 120-160 | | 1970-1982 |
| 2309 | Up to 2 discontinued colours | | 60-80 | 120-160 | | |
| 2464 | Percheron in show harness | 9¾ | 200-300 | 400-600 | | 1973-1982 |
| 2465 | Clydesdale in show or working harness | 10¾ | 150-200 | 300-400 | | 1973-1982 |
| 2548 | Small Shire (not put into production) | 6 | 400-500 | 800-1000 | | 1976 only |
| †2578 | Shire Horse with or without working harness | 8¼ | 89·95 | RRP | 62 | 1976-C |
| 2578 | Up to 3 discontinued colours | | 75-100 | 150-200 | | |
| **2914 | 'Spirit of Earth' | 7 | 40-60 | 80-120 | 61 | 1985-1993 |
| 2914 | Up to 6 discontinued colours | | 40-60 | 80-120 | | |

## Ponies

| Model No | Name of Model | Size inches | Current Value £ | US$ | DA Number | Production Period |
|---|---|---|---|---|---|---|
| 1033 | Shetland Pony | 5¾ | 23·95 | RRP | 47 | 1945-C |
| 1033 | Up to 5 discontinued colours | | 50-700 | 100-1400 | | |
| 1197 | Pony head up | 5½ | 50-75 | 100-150 | | 1950-1972 |
| 1197 | Up to 9 discontinued colours | | 75-500 | 150-1000 | | |
| 1480 | Pony (as 1500) | 4 | 100-125 | 200-250 | | 1957-1966 |
| 1480 | Up to 6 discontinued colours | | 125-500 | 250-1000 | | |
| 1483 | Pony (as 1499) | 5 | 100-125 | 200-250 | | 1957-1966 |
| 1483 | Up to 7 discontinued colours | | 125-500 | 250-1000 | | |
| 1641 | Connemara Pony 'Terese of Leam' | 7 | 100-120 | 200-240 | | 1959-1983 |
| 1642/1 | Dartmoor Pony 'Jentyl' | 6¼ | 75-100 | 150-200 | | 1959-1983 |
| ø1642/2 | Dartmoor Pony 'Warlord' | 6¼ | 45 | 90 | | 1996-1997 |
| 1643 | Welsh Mountain Pony 'Coed Coch Madog' | 6¼ | 100-125 | 200-250 | | 1959-1989 |
| 1644 | Highland Pony 'Mackinonneach' | 7¼ | 100-125 | 200-250 | | 1959-1989 |
| 1645 | Exmoor Pony 'Heatherman' | 6½ | 75-100 | 150-200 | | 1959-1984 |
| 1646 | New Forest Pony 'Jonathan 3rd' | 7 | 75-100 | 150-200 | | 1960-1983 |
| 1647 | Fell Pony 'Dene Dauntless' | 6¾ | 75-100 | 150-200 | | 1960-1982 |
| 1648 | Shetland Pony 'Eschon Chan Ronay' | 4¾ | 60-80 | 120-160 | | 1960-1989 |
| 1671 | Dales Pony 'Maisie' | 6½ | 100-125 | 200-250 | | 1960-1982 |
| 2468 | Icelandic Pony | — | 400-500 | 800-1000 | | 1973-1974 |
| øø | Dartmoor Pony (mare) 'Another Bunch' | 6 | 60 | 120 | | 1997-1998 |

| Model No | Name of Model | Size inches | Current Value £ | US$ | DA Number | Production Period |
|---|---|---|---|---|---|---|

## Wall Plaques of Horses

| Model No | Name of Model | Size inches | Current Value £ | US$ | DA Number | Production Period |
|---|---|---|---|---|---|---|
| 686 | Horse's Head through a horseshoe looking left | 7¼ x 6 | 50-60 | 100-120 | | 1939-1940 |
| 687 | Horse's Head through a horseshoe looking right | 7¼ x 6 | 50-60 | 100-120 | | 1939-1940 |
| 806 | Horse's Head Plaque (as 686 with raised back) | 7¼ x 6 | 50-60 | 100-120 | | 1940-1967 |
| 807 | Horse's Head Plaque (as 687 with raised back) | 7¼ x 6 | 50-60 | 100-120 | | 1940-1967 |
| 1382 | Hunter Horse Head | 4 x 4 | 40-60 | 80-120 | | 1955-1969 |
| 1384 | Palomino Horse Head | 4 x 4 | 40-60 | 80-120 | | 1955-1969 |
| 1385 | Arab Horse Head | 4 x 4 | 40-60 | 80-120 | | 1955-1969 |
| 1505 | Huntsman (as 868) Plaque | 10 | 200-250 | 400-500 | | 1957-1962 |
| 1513 | Lady on horse 'taking off' | 9 x 4¼ | 200-250 | 400-500 | | 1957-1962 |
| 1514 | Man on horse 'landing' | 8¾ x 7¾ | 200-250 | 400-500 | | 1957-1962 |
| 1515 | Lady on horse 'going over' | 8 x 5½ | 200-250 | 400-500 | | 1957-1962 |
| 2699 | 'Troy' (head only) on wood | 6 | 25-30 | 50-60 | | 1980-1989 |
| 2700 | 'Arkle' (head only) on wood | 6 | 25-30 | 50-60 | | 1980-1989 |
| 2701 | 'The Minstrel' (head only) on wood | 6 | 25-30 | 50-60 | | 1981-1989 |
| 2702 | 'Red Rum' (head only) on wood | 6 | 25-30 | 50-60 | | 1981-1989 |

*Carries a Beswick backstamp for 1994 only, thereafter the Royal Doulton mark will be used.
**Higher price for matt finish
†Current models matt only
øSpecial commission of 1500 pieces and carrying the Beswick backstamp.
øøSpecial commission of 1500 pieces and carrying the Beswick backstamp. This is a completely new model.

*The last production model of the Kitty McBride series, no **2589** and possibly harder to find than 'A Good Read'. Further models were planned, but a decision was made not to proceed with any more of the series.*

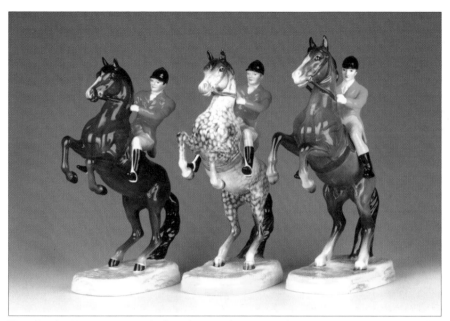

*Three Rearing Huntsmen **868**. L–R: Second version, brown; second version, rocking horse grey and first version, orange coat.*

*L–R: Connemara **1641** with a visitor from the Doulton stable, in the form of 'My First Horse' **DA193** (on a plinth) and the special commission Dartmoor Pony **1642/2** 'Warlord'.*

*The two Beswick Collectors Specials L–R: Standing Shire **818** and Trotting Shire **975**.*

*'Bois Boussel' **701** on 8" x 3" copper lustre base no **1809**.*

*Persian Cat **1880** in tabby.*

*Persian Cat **1898** in blue/grey.*

*Persian cat **1989** in tabby.*

*Persian cat **1876** in grey.*

*Cats Orchestra on a wood base **1026-1029**.*

*Siamese kittens in three colour variations – model **1296**.*

*The rare **301** Dog plaque – Sealyham.*

*Dog **308** in blue.*

*Connoisseur Basset Hound **2045**.*

*Brown and white colour trial **1378/5**.*

*Bassett Hound plaque **2235** in relief decoration, but with much of its black on-glaze colour missing.*

*Bookend **952/2** – front.*

*Bookend **952/2** – reverse.*

*Four of the cute characters from Beswick. L–R: Dusty Mole **1155**; Zimmy Lion **1150**; Mickey Mouse **1278** and Hazel Nutt **1153**.*

*The complete set of five Rupert figures.*

*Peter Rabbit and the Red Pocket Handkerchief showing his two gold buttons.*

*The two special commission Meerkats from UKI Ceramics. L–R: **3571** and **3568**.*

MRS. RABBIT AND
THE FOUR BUNNIES

*Mrs Rabbit and the Four Bunnies. The elusive special edition for 1997.*

*Tortoise family **1335-1337**.*

*Hen and Cock salt and pepper **1099** with the three chicks running **2200-2202**.*

*Yock-Yock and Peter Rabbit in the Watering Can from the Studio Sculpture series.*

*Kangerinie **1005**.*

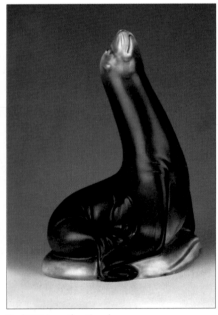

*Sussex Cockerel – a rare bird – **1899**.*

*Seal **383** in authentic colour.*

*Four of the hard-to-find Beatrix Potter figures. L–R: **2425** Sir Isaac Newton; **1105/1** Benjamin Bunny; **2061** Amiable Guinea Pig and **2508** Simpkin.*

*Three more of the hard-to-find Beatrix Potter's. L–R: **2601** Duchess with Pie; **2559** Ginger and **2334** Pickles.*

*The two versions of Fawn no **1000**.*

*Early Blue Budgerigar **1216** with hand crafted flowers.*

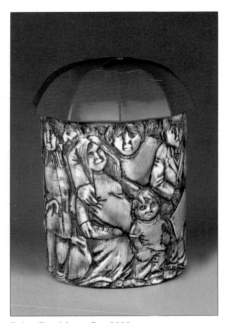

*Rainy Day Money Box **2808**.*

*L–R: Boy Hiker **1093** and Girl Hiker **1094**.*

*The very rare Beatrix Potter Wall Plaques **2085** and **2082**.*

*Laurel and Hardy cruet – with stand – **575**.*

*Colin Melbourne Poodle **1472**.*

*Angel Fish **1047**. The second fish to be modelled at Beswick.*

*The very rare Arctic Tern 768.*

*Table models of Standing Yachts. L–R: 1610 and 1634.*

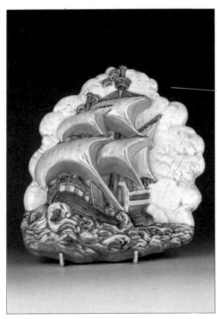

*'Galleon' wall plaque 263.*

*Large 'Fireside' Penguin 2357.*

*Four Dancers of the World. L–R: **1263** Indian; **1333** Chinese; **1320** Siamese; **1321** Japanese.*

*English Country Friends, Shephard Sheepdog **3422 (ECF 5)** with sheep and dog.*

63

*'Solid Friendship' catalogue special.*

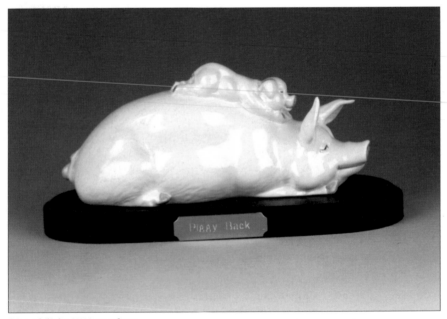

*Pig and Piglet* **2746**, *on a base.*

*The three Anglund Children. L–R: **2272**, **2293** and **2317**.*

*Babbity Bumble **2971**, Mr McGregor **3506** and Mother Ladybird **2966** from the Beatrix Potter Collection.*

*Regent Street wall plaque **2443**.*

*Stoat **1021** in his winter coat, painted in oils by Norma Cunningham.*

*Beswick Blue Donkey on base **369**.*

*The very impressive Studio Sculpture **SS13**, Swan.*

*Five out of the seven in the 'Top Cat' series. L–R: Brain; Fancy Fancy; Officer Dibble; Spook and Benny. Commissioned by Doulton and Beswick Fairs in England.*

*The Flintstones. L–R: Dino; Wilma; Pebbles; Fred; Barney; Bam-Bam and Betty. Commissioned by UK International Ceramics in a limited edition of 2000.*

*Tom from Tom & Jerry. Commissioned by UK International Ceramics in a limited edition of 2000.*

*Jerry from Tom & Jerry. Commissioned by UK International Ceramics in a limited edition of 2000.*

*Droopy. Commissioned by UK International Ceramics in a limited edition of 2000.*

*Fairy Drinking **1011** left and Fairy Crying **1010**, both extremely rare.*

*Three of the Little Likeables. L–R:* **LL6** *Fawn;* **LL8** *Cat's Chorus;* **LL7** *Duckling.*

*Three more Little Likeables, L–R:* **LL5** *Elephant;* **LL2** *Frog;* **LL1** *Hen and two chicks.*

*Fawnie **1003** in Beswick blue.*

***Lady** standing on base **442** (not a man as previously thought) in Beswick blue.*

*Lady wall mask **277**.*

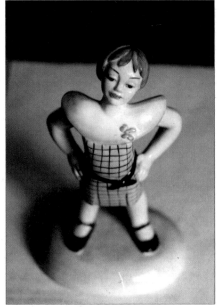

*Lady standing on base **442**, now with a name – Annabel.*

*The one that started it all. My first piece of Beswick, 802.*

*Model 831 – Dog with glasses – now long out of production.*

*Flopsy, Mopsy and Cottontail 1274, left is the thin base Beswick mark model (gold or brown) and right is the thick base Royal Albert model introduced in 1989. Close inspection reveals that the second version is a new model and not just a thicker base.*

*Two Spanish Children with Donkey* **1245**.

*Shetland Pony* **1033**, *looking very nice in its unusual colour.*

*Deer **2206** and Trout **2207** whisky flasks. Also found in blue.*

*Mr Micawber **310**. First version on the right, second version on the left.*

*Double Diamond lamp 1850.*

*A fully signed Colin Melbourne mark, with the standard Beswick stamp and paintress number.*

*Pig Prom. L–R: **PP9** Christopher; **PP8** Richard; **PP10** George (no 10 is exclusive to John Sinclair, limited edition of 2000).*

*868 Rearing Huntsman – first version – with orange coat and yellow jodhpurs.*

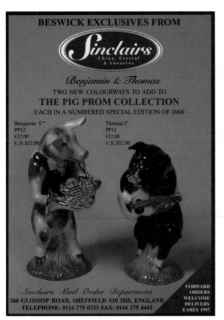

*Pig Prom. L–R: **PP12** Benjamin; **PP11** Thomas. Each is a numbered edition of 2000 and exclusive to John Sinclair.*

*Winston Churchill Character Jug **931**, complete with cover. This is sometimes missing.*

WALT DISNEY FIGURES
COPYRIGHT

THUMPER
1291–3¾"

PINOCCHIO
1282–4"

GOOFY
1281–4¼"

TINKERBELL
1312–5"

PETER PAN
1307–5"

JIMINY CRICKET
1279–4"

NANA
1301–3½"

SMEE
1302–4½"

MICKEY MOUSE 1278-3½"

PLUTO 1280–3½"

DONALD DUCK 1283–4"

MINNIE MOUSE 1289-4"

*Walt Disney Figures – Catalogue page.*

*A superb group of very collectable models from both the Beatrix Potter and Rupert series.*

*Mock Turtle* **2478**, *left and The Gryphon* **2485**, *both from the Alice in Wonderland series.*

*A Colin Melbourne group containing L–R: Bisons **1409/1414**; Horse **1411**; Cock **1467**; Cat **1412**; Bulldog **1463** and Dachshund **1469**.*

# Wild Animals

(All current Wild Animals carry a Beswick backstamp)

A trip to the zoo is an exciting day out for all the family and it would appear that the Beswick modellers have also been frequent visitors. The Lion and the Cheetah in the Connoisseur series were both modelled from animals at Dudley Zoo and the Panda (2613) was based on Chi-Chi at London Zoo.

There are over one hundred and thirty different models of which the largest and most spectacular must surely be the Indian Elephant with a tiger clawing its back and the smallest, the Mouse (1678). In between these there is a veritable Noah's Ark of very good quality, finely detailed animals. British wildlife and exotic species have co-existed in the collection over the years, giving animal lovers opportunities to specialise in either field. The Beswick modellers' interpretations have ranged from the cuddly Panda (1815) to realistic and superbly detailed Connoisseur models. Various different finishes have been offered in the Wild Animal collection, matt or glossy or, as in some of the earliest models, an all over blue glaze. Although these may lack the naturalism of later wild animals, they are still very appealing to collectors.

| Model No | Name of Model | Size inches | Current Value £ | US$ | DA No | Production Period |
|---|---|---|---|---|---|---|
| 315 | Squirrel on base | 8¾ | 100-150 | 200-300 | | 1935-1954 |
| 316 | Rabbit on base | 6¾ | 100-150 | 200-300 | | 1935-1954 |
| 368 | Frog on base | 6 | 100-150 | 200-300 | | 1936-1954 |
| 383 | Seal on base | 10 | 100-150 | 200-300 | | 1936-1954 |
| 397 | Monkey on base | 7 | 100-125 | 200-250 | | 1936-1954 |
| 417 | Polar Bear on base | 6¼ | 100-125 | 200-250 | | 1936-1954 |
| 568 | Elephant | 9 | 75-100 | 150-200 | | 1938-1954 |
| 569 | Elephant | 4¾ | 50-75 | 100-150 | | 1938-1954 |
| 692 | Elephant | 4¼ | 50-75 | 100-150 | | 1939-1954 |
| 696 | Fawn standing on base Also in Flambé | 7½ | 75-100 | 150-200 | | 1939-1954 |
| 709 | Beaver | — | 100-150 | 200-300 | | 1939-1954 |
| 711 | Panda | 4½ | 50-75 | 100-150 | | 1939-1940 |
| 720 | Panda Baby | 3¾ | 40-50 | 80-100 | | 1939-1954 |
| 721 | Fawn lying on base | 4½ | 75-100 | 150-200 | | 1939-1954 |
| 738 | Panda Mother with ball | 4½ | 50-75 | 100-150 | | 1939-1954 |
| 823 | Rabbit | 3 | 15-20 | 30-40 | | 1940-1971 |
| 824 | Rabbit | 2¼ | 15-20 | 30-40 | | 1940-1971 |
| 825 | Rabbit | 1⅜ | 10-15 | 20-30 | | 1940-1971 |
| 826 | Rabbit | 2 | 10-15 | 20-30 | | 1940-1971 |
| 828/1 | Elephant | 6 | 50-75 | 100-150 | | 1940-1960 |
| 828/2 | Elephant | 4½ | 40-60 | 80-120 | | 1940-1960 |
| 828/3 | Elephant | 3 | 40-60 | 80-120 | | 1940-1960 |
| 830 | Lizard | 7 | 75-100 | 150-200 | | 1940-1954 |
| 841 | Leopard sitting | 6½ | 100-150 | 200-300 | | 1940-1954 |
| 845 | Zebra (black stripes on white body) | 7¼ | 100-125 | 200-250 | | 1940-1969 |
| 845 | Zebra (black stripes on orange body) | 7¼ | 200-250 | 400-500 | | 1940-1958 |
| 853 | Giraffe | 7¼ | 100-150 | 200-300 | | 1940-1975 |
| 954 | Stag lying | 5½ | 50-75 | 100-150 | | 1941-1975 |
| ***974 | Elephant | 4¾ | 40-50 | 80-100 | | 1942-1996 |

| Model No | Name of Model | Size inches | Current Value £ | US$ | DA No | Production Period |
|---|---|---|---|---|---|---|
| ***981 | Stag | 8 | 25·95 | RRP | | 1942-C |
| ø998 | Elephant | 10¼ | 150-175 | 300-350 | | 1943-1975 |
| ***999 | Doe | 6 | 19·95 | RRP | | 1943-C |
| 1000/1 | Fawn (tail up, legs straight) | 3½ | 30-40 | 60-80 | | 1943-1955 |
| ***1000/2 | Fawn (tail down, legs splayed) | 3½ | 12·95 | RRP | | 1955-C |
| 1007 | Squirrel standing | 2¼ | 30-40 | 60-80 | | 1944-1965 |
| 1008 | Squirrel lying | 1¾ | 30-40 | 60-80 | | 1944-1965 |
| 1009 | Squirrel cracking nut | 4½ | 60-80 | 120-160 | | 1944-1965 |
| ***1016 | Fox standing | 5½ | 21·50 | RRP | | 1945-C |
| ***1017 | Fox lying | 1¾ | 40-50 | | | 1945-1996 |
| 1019 | Bison | 5¾ | 100-125 | 200-250 | | 1945-1973 |
| 1021 | Stoat in winter or summer coat | 5½ | 250-300 | 500-800 | | 1945-1973 |
| 1024 | Hare running on base | 5¼ | 250-300 | 500-800 | | 1945-1962 |
| 1025 | Hare sitting | 7 | 250-300 | 500-800 | | 1945-1962 |
| 1038 | Koala Bear | 3½ | 30-40 | 60-80 | | 1945-1971 |
| 1039 | Koala Bear | 2¼ | 25-30 | 50-60 | | 1945-1972 |
| 1040 | Koala Bear | 2¼ | 25-30 | 50-60 | | 1945-1972 |
| 1043 | Camel Foal | 5 | 60-80 | 120-160 | | 1946-1971 |
| 1044 | Camel | 7 | 100-125 | 200-250 | | 1946-1972 |
| 1048 | Springbok | 7¼ | 200-250 | 400-500 | | 1946-1962 |
| 1082 | Leopard | 4¾ | 75-100 | 150-200 | | 1946-1975 |
| 1089 | Koala Bear | 3½ | 30-40 | 60-80 | | 1947-1971 |
| 1160 | Kangaroo | 5¾ | 75-100 | 150-200 | | 1949-1965 |
| 1308 | Skunk | 2¾ | 80-100 | 160-200 | | 1953-1962 |
| 1309 | Skunk | 1½ | 40-60 | 80-120 | | 1953-1962 |
| 1310 | Skunk | 2 | 40-60 | 80-120 | | 1953-1962 |
| 1313 | Bear (on all fours) (black or brown) | 2½ | 50-75 | 100-150 | | 1953-1973 |
| 1314 | Bear standing (black or brown) | 4½ | 50-75 | 100-150 | | 1953-1973 |
| 1315 | Baby Bear sitting (black or brown) | 2¼ | 40-60 | 80-120 | | 1953-1973 |
| 1409 | Bison (CM series) | 10½ | 200-250 | 400-500 | | 1956-1963 |
| 1414 | Bison small (CM series) | 8¾ | 150-200 | 300-400 | | 1956-1970 |
| 1418 | Fox (CM series) | 8 long | 150-200 | 300-400 | | 1956-1970 |
| • 1419 | Lion (CM series) | 5¼ | 200-250 | 400-500 | | 1956-1962 |
| ***1440 | Fox (small) | 2½ | 9·95 | RRP | | 1956-C |
| 1465 | Zebra (CM series) | 6 | 150-200 | 300-400 | | 1956-1970 |
| 1468 | Bison (CM series) | — | 100-150 | 200-300 | | 1956-1970 |
| 1475 | Fox (CM series) | 10 long | 200-250 | 400-500 | | 1957-1970 |
| 1481 | Reindeer (CM series) | 5½ | 250-300 | 500-600 | | 1957-1970 |
| 1486 | Tigress | 4¼ | 60-80 | 120-160 | | 1957-1975 |
| 1506 | Lion (face to front) | 5¼ | 40-60 | 80-120 | | 1957-1967 |
| 1507 | Lioness | 4¾ | 40-60 | 80-120 | | 1957-1967 |
| 1508 | Lion Cub | 3¾ | 30-40 | 60-80 | | 1957-1967 |
| 1532 | Hippopotamus | 3½ | 100-125 | 200-250 | | 1958-1966 |
| 1533 | Polar Bear | 4¾ | 100-125 | 200-250 | | 1958-1966 |
| 1534 | Seal | 3 | 80-100 | 160-200 | | 1958-1966 |
| 1551 | Chamois | 4 | 30-35 | 60-70 | | 1958-1971 |
| 1597 | Baby Giraffe | 4¼ | 30-35 | 60-70 | | 1959-1971 |
| 1631 | Giraffe (large) | 12 | 150-200 | 300-400 | | 1959-1975 |
| 1678 | Mouse (see 1677 Cats) | 2½ | 7·95 | RRP | | 1960-C |
| 1688 | Reindeer | 3¾ | 30-35 | 60-70 | | 1960-1971 |
| ø1702 | Puma, tawny, on rock | 8½ | 100-120 | 200-240 | | 1960-1989 |
| | also in black | 8½ | 120-140 | 240-280 | | 1960-1975 |
| 1720 | Indian Elephant & Tiger | 12 | 250-300 | 500-600 | | 1960-1975 |
| ***1748 | Fox sitting | 3 | 9·95 | RRP | | 1961-C |

| Model No | Name of Model | Size inches | Current Value £ | US$ | DA No | Production Period |
|---|---|---|---|---|---|---|
| ø1770 | Indian Elephant (as model 1720) | 12 | 150-175 | 300-375 | | 1961-1982 |
| ***1815 | Panda | 2¼ | 8·95 | RRP | | 1962-C |
| 1823 | Puma, tawny, on rock (small) | 6 | 80-100 | 160-200 | | 1962-1975 |
| | also in black | 6 | 100-120 | 200-240 | | 1962-1975 |
| 1943 | Beaver | 2½ | 125-150 | 250-300 | | 1964-1967 |
| 2089 | Lion (face to side) | 5½ | 40-60 | 80-120 | | 1967-1983 |
| ø2090 | Moose | 6¼ | 250-300 | 500-600 | | 1968-1973 |
| 2093 | Old Staffordshire Lion | 5¾ | 150-175 | 300-350 | | 1967-1969 |
| 2094 | Old Staffordshire Unicorn | 6 | 150-175 | 300-350 | | 1967-1969 |
| ***2096 | Tiger | 7½ | 40-60 | 80-120 | | 1967-1989 |
| 2097 | Lioness | 5¾ | 40-60 | 80-120 | | 1967-1983 |
| 2098 | Lion Cub | 4 | 30-40 | 60-80 | | 1967-1982 |
| 2182 | Heraldic Unicorn on base | 8½ | 150-175 | 300-350 | | 1968-1969 |
| 2194 | Racoon | 4¼ | 175-200 | 350-400 | | 1968-1973 |
| 2195 | Beaver | 4⅜ | 175-200 | 350-400 | | 1968-1973 |
| 2222 | Lion with crown | 5¼ | 150-175 | 300-350 | | 1968-1969 |
| 2223 | Unicorn | 5¼ | 150-175 | 300-350 | | 1968-1969 |
| øø2253 | Hedgehog ('Moda' range) | 3½ | 40-50 | 80-100 | | 1969-1971 |
| 2302 | Mouse (see 2301 Cats) | 1¾ | 20-30 | 40-60 | | 1969-1971 |
| 2312 | Kangaroo (small) | 4⅞ | 100-125 | 200-250 | | 1970-1971 |
| 2348 | Fox | 12¼ | 175-200 | 350-400 | | 1970-1983 |
| 2554 | Lion | 6½ | 40-60 | 80-120 | | 1983-1994 |
| *2613 | Panda 'Chi-Chi' sitting with bamboo shoot | 3¾ | 60-80 | 120-160 | | 1978-1980 |
| øø2629 | Stag | 13½ | 75-100 | 150-200 | 32 | 1978-1996 |
| øø2725 | Cheetah on Rock | 6½ | 75-100 | 150-200 | 39 | 1981-1994 |
| øø2933 | Lion Head | 6 | 25-30 | 50-60 | | 1985-1989 |
| øø2934 | Tiger Head | 6 | 25-30 | 50-60 | | 1985-1989 |
| øø2936 | Stag Head | 6 | 25-30 | 50-60 | | 1985-1989 |
| **2944 | Panda sitting without bamboo shoot | 3¾ | 25-30 | 50-60 | | 1986-1987 |
| 3009 | Cheetah | 5 | 40-60 | 80-120 | | 1986-1994 |
| 3014 | Two Koala Bears on branch (not put into production) | 5 | 100-150 | 200-300 | | 1986 only |
| 3392 | Badger (cub) | 2 | 9·95 | RRP | | 1994-C |
| 3393 | Badger (male) | 2¼ | 13·50 | RRP | | 1994-C |
| 3394 | Badger (female) | 2¼ | 13·50 | RRP | | 1994-C |
| 3397 | Harvest Mouse | 2½ | 11·95 | RRP | | 1994-C |
| 3399 | Woodmouse | 3¼ | 11·95 | RRP | | 1994-C |

*For London Zoo and gloss finish only
**For WWF and matt finish only
***Available in matt finish 1985-1988
øAvailable in matt finish 1970-1972
øøMatt finish only

# Part Two: Character Wares

## Character and Toby Jugs, Teapots and Derivatives

(All these models carry a Beswick backstamp)

The idea of modelling a jug in the form of a human head is a very ancient one and it occurs with regularity throughout the history of ceramics. In the early 1930s there was a revival of interest in the face jug pioneered by the Royal Doulton potteries and the Beswick modellers were quick to respond to this new collecting interest. Their first character jug, **Tony Weller**, was introduced in 1935 and other Dickens personalities soon followed. During the war some patriotic character jugs were produced, promoting the endeavours of the army, navy and airforce but the Dickens theme was resumed after hostilities had ended. In 1967 two Shakespearean characters joined the throng but production was short lived.

The Beswick character jugs had all been withdrawn by 1973 but the skills of the craftsmen involved have not gone to waste. Today the Beswick studio, as part of the Royal Doulton group, is responsible for the production of all Character Jugs with a Royal Doulton backstamp.

## Toby Jugs

The Toby differs from the character jug in that the whole figure is modelled into jug form not just the head and shoulders. The Toby has become a popular ornament in the drinking houses of Britain and is highly valued by many collectors. Of the six very attractive models which Beswick have produced, three are traditional types in which Toby Phillpot, a character in a popular eighteenth century drinking song, sits with a jug of ale in one hand and a tankard in the other.

The topers were soon joined by other congenial characters. **The Midshipman** playing the violin was a popular subject in the 1770s and Beswick produced a faithful version of him in 1948. The **Martha Gunn** Toby was also inspired by an eighteenth century original by Ralph Wood. She was the bathing attendant at Brighton beach who supposedly taught King George IV to swim.

Famous characters of the twentieth century have also been portrayed in Toby form and **Winston Churchill** has probably been most 'honoured' in this way. During the war Beswick introduced a very fine image of him which was only available until 1954.

All of these jugs can be classed as rare and are very hard to find today in good condition.

## Derivatives

The popular Dickens personalities were not confined to character jugs. It was possible to deck out the tea table with useful Dickens wares — a **Dolly Varden** teapot with perhaps a **Pecksniff** cream jug and a **Pickwick** sugar bowl. Jam could be discreetly contained in a **Tony Weller** preserve pot and for extra spice the **Sairey Gamp** pepper pot and **Mr Micawber** salt pot could be on hand. These were all the specialities of Mr Gredington who offered alternative favourite characters.

It is doubtful whether any of these entertaining characters serve their original purpose today as they are quite popular with collectors.

| Model No | Name of Model | | Height inches | Current Value £ | US$ | Production Period |
|---|---|---|---|---|---|---|
| 281/1 | Tony Weller (Yellow hat and black band) | CJ | 7 | 50-60 | 100-120 | 1935-1940 |
| 281/2 | Tony Weller (all green hat) | CJ | 7 | 40-50 | 80-100 | 1940-1970 |
| 281/3 | Tony Weller (re-modelled) (Yellow hat band on olive green) | CJ | 6¾ | 65-75 | 130-150 | 1970-1973 |
| 310/1 | Micawber (Black hat) | CJ | 8¾ | 50-60 | 100-120 | 1935-1940 |
| 310/2 | Micawber (Green hat) | CJ | 8¾ | 40-50 | 80-100 | 1940-1970 |
| 310/3 | Micawber (re-modelled) (Olive green hat) | CJ | 6¾ | 65-75 | 130-150 | 1970-1973 |
| 371 | Sairey Gamp | CJ | 6½ | 40-50 | 80-100 | 1936-1973 |
| 372 | Scrooge | CJ | 7 | 40-50 | 80-100 | 1936-1973 |
| 575 | Laurel & Hardy cruet & base | | 4½ | 65-85 | 130-170 | 1938-1969 |
| 673 | Tony Weller sugar | | 2¾ | 15-20 | 30-40 | 1939-1973 |
| 674 | Mr Micawber cream | | 3¼ | 15-20 | 30-40 | 1939-1973 |
| 689 | Sairey Gamp pepper | | 2½ | 15-20 | 30-40 | 1939-1973 |
| 690 | Mr Micawber salt | | 3½ | 15-20 | 30-40 | 1939-1973 |
| 691 | Sairey Gamp teapot | | 5¾ | 65-75 | 130-150 | 1939-1973 |
| 735 | Old Bill | CJ | 5 | 100-125 | 200-250 | 1939-1954 |

*Thelwell's Pony Express, in grey, **2789**.*

| Model No | Name of Model | | Height inches | Current Value £ | US$ | Production Period |
|---|---|---|---|---|---|---|
| 736 | Navy | CJ | 5 | 100-125 | 200-250 | 1939-1954 |
| 737 | Air Force | CJ | 5 | 120-125 | 240-250 | 1939-1954 |
| 742 | Panda teapot | | 6 | 75-100 | 150-200 | 1939-1954 |
| 931 | Winston Churchill & lid | TJ | 7 | 200-250 | 400-500 | 1941-1954 |
| 1110 | Toby Phillpot | TJ | 8 | 75-85 | 150-175 | 1948-1973 |
| 1111 | Toby Phillpot | TJ | 6½ | 65-75 | 130-150 | 1948-1973 |
| 1112 | Midshipman Toby | TJ | 5¼ | 125-150 | 250-300 | 1948-1973 |
| 1113 | Martha Gunn holding jug | TJ | 3½ | 75-100 | 150-200 | 1948-1962 |
| 1114 | Toby Sitting on Barrel holding jug | TJ | 3½ | 75-100 | 150-200 | 1948-1962 |
| 1116 | Peggoty teapot | | 6 | 75-85 | 150-170 | 1948-1973 |
| 1117 | Pecksniff cream | | 3½ | 15-20 | 30-40 | 1948-1973 |
| 1118 | Pickwick sugar | | 3 | 15-20 | 30-40 | 1948-1967 |
| 1119 | Pickwick cream | | 3¼ | 15-20 | 30-40 | 1948-1973 |
| 1120 | Captain Cuttle | CJ | 4½ | 40-45 | 80-90 | 1948-1973 |
| 1121 | Barnaby Rudge | CJ | 4½ | 40-45 | 80-90 | 1948-1969 |
| 1129 | Pecksniff sugar | | 3½ | 15-20 | 30-40 | 1948-1967 |
| 1203 | Dolly Varden teapot | | 6¼ | 100-125 | 200-250 | 1950-1973 |
| 1204 | Mr Varden cream | | 3½ | 25-30 | 50-60 | 1950-1973 |
| 1205 | Mrs Varden sugar | | 3 | 25-30 | 50-60 | 1950-1967 |
| 1206 | Sairey Gamp preserve & lid | | 3 | 30-35 | 60-70 | 1950-1967 |
| 1207 | Tony Weller preserve & lid | | 3 | 30-35 | 60-70 | 1950-1967 |
| 1369 | Sam Weller teapot | | 6¼ | 125-150 | 250-300 | 1955-1973 |
| 2030 | Martin Chuzzlewit | CJ | 4¾ | 60-75 | 120-150 | 1966-1973 |
| 2031 | Little Nell's Grandfather | CJ | 5⅜ | 60-75 | 120-150 | 1966-1973 |
| 2032 | Mr Bumble | CJ | 4⅞ | 60-75 | 120-150 | 1966-1973 |
| 2075 | Betsy Trotwood | CJ | 5 | 60-75 | 120-150 | 1967-1973 |
| 2095 | Falstaff | CJ | 6¾ | 75-100 | 150-200 | 1968-1973 |
| 2099 | Henry VIII | CJ | 7 | 75-100 | 150-200 | 1968-1973 |
| 3105 | Panda teapot | | 6 | 35-45 | 70-90 | 1989-1990 |
| *3138 | Cat teapot (white) | | 6 | 35-45 | 70-90 | 1989-1990 |
| 3139 | Mouse teapot | | 7 | 35-45 | 70-90 | 1989-1990 |
| 3142 | Squirrel teapot | | 7 | 35-45 | 70-90 | 1989-1990 |

CJ Character Jug    TJ Toby Jug

*Small number available in black and white at a higher price

# Characters from Film and Literature

(All models produced up to August 1989 carry a Beswick stamp. All current models produced since August 1989 carry a Royal Albert stamp)

Over the years, the Beswick modellers have turned the pages of many children's classics and brought a new dimension to the memorable illustrations, so that as well as enjoying the books, young readers could surround themselves with little models of their favourite characters. The timeless quality of many Victorian and Edwardian children's books makes them a fertile source of inspiration and Beswick modellers have had particular success with their interpretations of Alice in Wonderland and the tales of Beatrix Potter.

The first Beatrix Potter figure was suggested by Mrs Lucy Beswick, wife of Ewart, when she mentioned to Jim Hayward in 1947 that Jemima Puddleduck might be a good subject for a figure. When Jim Hayward took up her suggestion, copies of the Beatrix Potter tales belonging to her daughter Judith soon disappeared into the design studio. The result was so successful that a whole range of character studies from the tales of Beatrix Potter followed.

This extract from *The Publishers' Circular and Booksellers' Record* of July 1950 gives an indication of the popularity of the Beatrix Potter figures: "These little figures are creating a buying craze which is sweeping through the United States of America and Canada. This well known pottery firm first issued twelve of these charming china figures, each being about three and three quarter inches high, beautifully fashioned and coloured after the famous illustrations from Beatrix Potter's works. The colourings are full, the figures most natural and the whole present beautiful objects d'art."

Today a new figure may be suggested from the illustrations in the books — perhaps a popular character such as Peter Rabbit or Benjamin Bunny in a change of clothes or a different pose. Alternatively, the name of a character not previously illustrated such as Cottontail might suggest a study for designers in the studio. Any new ideas are discussed by the design manager and the modeller and several drawings and trial models follow. The figure must agree with the original book illustrations in every detail and so meticulous is the process that it can take six months or even longer for a model to be completed.

Following the success of the Beatrix Potter figures, Beswick started to introduce other characters from literature and film. In 1949 they introduced Zimmy the Lion, the star of **The Lion** cartoon released by the Rank Film Organisation in 1948. This character was the creation of David Hand, an ex-director at Walt Disney and such was Zimmy's success with his audience that sequel cartoons soon appeared introducing his friends Ginger Nutt, Hazel Nutt, Dinkum Platypus, Loopy Hare, Oscar Ostrich and Dusty Mole. Arthur Gredington added all these cartoon characters to the Beswick collection.

In 1952, the most famous cartoon character of all, Walt Disney's Mickey Mouse, was portrayed by Miss Granoska. Such was the popularity of Mickey and his friends that these Beswick figures are now very hard to find indeed in spite of being in production for twelve years. Also elusive are Snow White and the Seven Dwarfs which were introduced in 1954.

It was fourteen years before Beswick returned to the world of children for inspiration. Prompted by the success of Walt Disney's film version of A. A. Milne's *Winnie the Pooh*, Albert Hallam modelled a series of characters in 1968. Pooh Bear himself and Piglet must be the best known of this group along with Christopher Robin, a central character in all the books. All of these figures are now out of production and their appealing modelling makes them well worth collecting.

Another famous bear portrayed by Beswick was originally created by Mary Tourtel in 1920 but it was Alfred Bestall who popularised him in the first *Rupert Annual* published by the *Daily Express* newspaper in 1936. All of the stories and drawings in this annual were the work of Alfred Bestall who continued to write illustrated stories every year until 1973. Rupert Bear and his friends Algy Pug and Bill Badger were introduced in 1982 and have now been withdrawn.

One of the best known children's classics which has inspired the Beswick artists is *Alice's Adventures in Wonderland* by Lewis Carroll. It would seem that they referred to the original drawings by John Tenniel in the 1865 edition of this book when creating their set of eleven colourful characters. The Mad Hatter and Alice herself are particularly attractive and difficult to find.

Unlike the characters from Alice in Wonderland, Beatrix Potter and Rupert Bear, Beswick's Thelwell collection is not based on illustrations from children's stories but on a series of cartoons for *Punch* magazine. The girl and pony theme of Norman Thelwell's drawings was inspired by an incident he observed from his window. Two small podgy girls, hard hats rammed down over their ears, approached a shaggy pony well known for his uncertain temper. They calmly marched towards him, pulled his tail, cracked his nose with a crop and so made the pony their obedient servant before his astonishment had time to turn to fury. The Beswick models, first introduced in 1982 and modelled by David Lyttleton, capture the humour portrayed in Thelwell's pony cartoons.

The Beswick artists have had a long standing ability to portray character and humour and this is very much in evidence, not only in the Thelwell collection but in all their portrayals of characters from children's stories and cartoons.

Another children's classic has been interpreted by the Beswick modellers, but for various reasons the series was only available for between two and three years.

The four main characters in Kenneth Graham's story *The Wind in the Willows*, were Toad, Badger, Mole and Ratty and models of each were introduced in 1987, to be followed by Portly (Otter) and Weasel Gamekeeper in 1988. They were all withdrawn at the end of 1989.

The Royal Albert backstamp was used and each figure was allocated a model number in the Beswick pattern book. Details are given in the listings, together with the Royal Albert number.

This set came out at the same time as the decision was made, by Royal Doulton, to change the backstamp of Beatrix Potter figures from Beswick to Royal Albert.

It is probable that this Brand name was thought to have more appeal, particularly to overseas markets.

To celebrate this change, Lawleys commissioned Royal Albert to produce six Beatrix Potter models with a gold backstamp and these are now extremely had to find because of the small number made.

The actual changeover date was set at 1st August, 1989, but it was obviously going to take some time for existing Beswick-marked models to clear the factory warehouse and be replaced by Royal Albert marked models.

It is believed that the highest number B.P. model to carry the Beswick mark is 3103, Tom Kitten character jug and the highest number figure to be 3094, Johnny Townmouse and Bag.

Model number 3157, Peter in the Gooseberry Net, is therefore the first B.P. model never to have carried the Beswick stamp.

In the listings, all B.P. models, from 3157 onwards, carry the Royal Albert mark and the number quoted is the Beswick pattern book model number. This number is also used in the currently published price list.

There are, however two exceptions. The large size Peter Rabbit and Jemima Puddleduck figures only carried the Beswick mark for the first year of production, thereafter changing to Royal Albert. There were also three others which due to delayed production, B.P. models 2965/66/71 were not introduced until after the backstamp changes had been made and they have therefore only carried the Royal Albert mark.

The popular Beswick gold backstamp was in use until 1971, when the brown printed transfer was substituted. It is believed that 2381 Pig Wig is the highest numbered Model to carry a gold backstamp. These gold backstamp Beatrix Potter models usually command a higher price than those marked with the Brown backstamp and this often means that the basic price is doubled.

In 1987 the three new BP character jugs models 2959/2960/3006 had a new style of backstamp where the printed word 'BESWICK' was replaced by the written words John Beswick.

In 1988 the three new BP character jugs 3088/3102/3103 and three new BP figures 3090/3091/3094 all had a different style of backstamp, where the written words John Beswick were followed by the printed words 'STUDIO OF ROYAL DOULTON, ENGLAND'.

The other three new BP figures introduced in 1988 — 2989/2996/3030 — all carried the standard printed 'BESWICK' mark. All now carry the Royal Albert stamp.

## Beatrix Potter – Figures

There are very many variations of backstamp which have been used on these very popular models since their introduction in late 1947. So as to simplify the listings, I have used the following method of identifying how long each type of backstamp was in use:

G.B.S. = Gold Beswick Stamp. 1947-1971
B.B.S. = Brown Beswick Stamp. 1972-1987
J.B.S. = John Beswick Stamp (with or without 'Studio of Royal Doulton'). 1988-1989
R.A.G. = Royal Albert Gold. 1989 only
R.A.B. = Royal Albert Brown. 1989 onwards
B.B.P.R = Brown Beswick Peter Rabbit. 1992 onwards
G.B.J.P. = Gold Beswick Jemima Puddleduck. 1994 only

I have not attempted, here, to record all the minor changes in wording and style, which have been used over the years.

Full details of these will be found in Louise Irvine's book *John Beswick & Royal Albert, Beatrix Potter Figures and Giftware*, published in 1996 by UK International Ceramics.

| Model No | Name of Model | Height inches | Current Value £ | US$ | Production Period | Back-stamp |
|---|---|---|---|---|---|---|
| 1092/1 | Jemima Puddleduck (2 in short base) | $4\frac{1}{4}$ | 60-70 | 120-140 | 1947-1971 | G.B.S. |
| | | | 30-35 | 60-70 | 1947-1971 | B.B.S. |
| 1092/2 | Jemima Puddleduck ($2\frac{1}{4}$ in long base) | $4\frac{1}{4}$ | 25-30 | 50-60 | 1983-1987 | B.B.S. |
| | | | 25-30 | 50-60 | 1988-1989 | J.B.S. |
| | | | 45-50 | 90-100 | 1989 only | R.A.G. |
| | | | 15·95 | RRP | 1989-C | R.A.B. |
| 1098/1 | Peter Rabbit (2 in short base) | $4\frac{1}{2}$ | 60-70 | 120-140 | 1947-1971 | G.B.S. |
| | | | 30-35 | 60-70 | 1972-1983 | B.B.S. |
| 1098/2 | Peter Rabbit ($2\frac{3}{8}$ in long base) | $4\frac{1}{2}$ | 25-30 | 50-60 | 1983-1987 | B.B.S. |
| | | | 25-30 | 50-60 | 1988-1989 | J.B.S. |
| | | | 45-50 | 90-100 | 1989 only | R.A.G. |
| | | | 15·95 | RRP | 1989-C | R.A.B. |
| 1100 | Tom Kitten | $3\frac{1}{2}$ | 60-70 | 120-140 | 1947-1971 | G.B.S. |
| | | | 30-35 | 60-70 | 1972-1987 | B.B.S. |
| | | | 30-35 | 60-70 | 1988-1989 | J.B.S. |
| | | | 15·95 | RRP | 1989-C | R.A.B. |
| 1101 | Timmy Tiptoes | $3\frac{3}{4}$ | 60-70 | 120-140 | 1948-1971 | G.B.S. |
| | | | 30-35 | 60-70 | 1972-1987 | B.B.S. |
| | | | 30-35 | 60-70 | 1988-1989 | J.B.S. |
| | | | 15·95 | RRP | 1989-C | R.A.B. |
| 1102 | Squirrel Nutkin | $3\frac{3}{4}$ | 60-70 | 120-140 | 1948-1971 | G.B.S. |
| | | | 30-35 | 60-70 | 1972-1987 | B.B.S. |
| | | | 30-35 | 60-70 | 1988-1989 | J.B.S. |
| | | | 15·95 | RRP | 1989-C | R.A.B. |
| 1103 | Mrs Tittlemouse | $3\frac{3}{4}$ | 60-70 | 120-140 | 1948-1971 | G.B.S. |
| | | | 30-35 | 60-70 | 1972-1987 | B.B.S. |
| | | | 30-35 | 60-70 | 1988-1989 | J.B.S. |
| | | | 25-30 | 50-60 | 1989-1993 | R.A.B. |
| 1104/1 | Little Pig Robinson (Blue striped smock) | 4 | 80-90 | 160-180 | 1948-1971 | G.B.S. |
| | | | 40-45 | 80-90 | 1972-1974 | B.B.S. |
| 1104/2 | Little Pig Robinson (Blue checked smock) | 4 | 30-35 | 60-70 | 1974-1987 | B.B.S. |
| | | | 30-35 | 60-70 | 1988-1989 | J.B.S. |
| | | | 15·95 | RRP | 1989-C | R.A.B. |
| 1105/1 | Benjamin Bunny (arms & slippers held away & ears protrude beyond hat) | 4 | 250-300 | 500-600 | 1948-1971 | G.B.S. |
| | | | 150-175 | 300-350 | 1972-1974 | B.B.S. |
| 1105/2 | Benjamin Bunny (arms & slippers flush to body & ears protrude beyond hat) | 4 | 125-150 | 250-300 | 1974-1983 | B.B.S. |
| 1105/3 | Benjamin Bunny (arms & slipper flush to body & ears do not protrude) | 4 | 30-35 | 60-70 | 1983-1987 | B.B.S. |
| | | | 30-35 | 60-70 | 1988-1989 | J.B.S. |
| | | | 45-50 | 90-100 | 1989-only | R.A.G. |
| | | | 15·95 | RRP | 1989-C | R.A.B. |
| 1106 | Samuel Whiskers | $3\frac{1}{2}$ | 60-70 | 120-140 | 1948-1971 | G.B.S. |
| | | | 30-35 | 60-70 | 1972-1987 | B.B.S. |
| | | | 30-35 | 60-70 | 1988-1989 | J.B.S. |
| | | | 25-30 | 50-60 | 1989-1995 | R.A.B. |
| 1107/1 | Mrs Tiggy Winkle (angled stripes to blouse) | $3\frac{1}{4}$ | 80-100 | 160-200 | 1948-1971 | G.B.S. |
| | | | 40-50 | 80-100 | 1972-1975 | B.B.S. |
| 1107/2 | Mrs Tiggy Winkle (vertical stripes to blouse) | $3\frac{1}{4}$ | 30-35 | 60-70 | 1975-1987 | B.B.S. |
| | | | 30-35 | 60-70 | 1988-1989 | J.B.S. |
| | | | 15·95 | RRP | 1989-C | R.A.B. |
| 1108 | Tailor of Gloucester | $3\frac{3}{4}$ | 60-70 | 120-140 | 1948-1971 | G.B.S. |
| | | | 30-35 | 60-70 | 1972-1987 | B.B.S. |
| | | | 30-35 | 60-70 | 1988-1989 | J.B.S. |
| | | | 15·95 | RRP | 1989-C | R.A.B. |

| Model No | Name of Model | Height inches | Current Value £ | US$ | Production Period | Back-stamp |
|---|---|---|---|---|---|---|
| 1109 | Timmy Willie | 3 | 60-70 | 120-140 | 1948-1971 | G.B.S. |
| | | | 30-35 | 60-70 | 1972-1987 | B.B.S. |
| | | | 30-35 | 60-70 | 1988-1989 | J.B.S. |
| | | | 25-30 | 50-60 | 1989-1993 | R.A.B. |
| 1157/1 | Jeremy Fisher (spotted body) | 3 | 100-120 | 200-240 | 1950-1971 | G.B.S. |
| | | | 40-50 | 80-100 | 1972-1983 | B.B.S. |
| 1157/2 | Jeremy Fisher (striped body) | 3 | 30-35 | 60-70 | 1983-1987 | B.B.S. |
| | | | 30-35 | 60-70 | 1988-1989 | J.B.S. |
| | | | 15·95 | RRP | 1989-C | R.A.B. |
| 1183 | Lady Mouse | 4 | 80-100 | 160-200 | 1950-1971 | G.B.S. |
| | | | 40-50 | 80-100 | 1972-1987 | B.B.S. |
| | | | 40-50 | 80-100 | 1988-1989 | J.B.S. |
| | | | 15·95 | RRP | 1989-C | R.A.B. |
| 1198 | Hunca Munca | $2\frac{3}{4}$ | 60-70 | 120-140 | 1951-1971 | G.B.S. |
| | | | 30-35 | 60-70 | 1972-1987 | B.B.S. |
| | | | 30-35 | 60-70 | 1988-1989 | J.B.S. |
| | | | 45-50 | 90-100 | 1989 only | R.A.G. |
| | | | 15·95 | RRP | 1989-C | R.A.B. |
| 1199 | Mrs Ribby | $3\frac{1}{2}$ | 70-80 | 140-160 | 1951-1971 | G.B.S. |
| | | | 35-40 | 70-80 | 1972-1987 | B.B.S. |
| | | | 35-40 | 70-80 | 1988-1989 | J.B.S. |
| | | | 15·95 | RRP | 1989-C | R.A.B. |
| 1200/1 | Mrs Rabbit (brolly sticks out) | $4\frac{1}{4}$ | 150-175 | 300-350 | 1951-1971 | G.B.S. |
| | | | 75-85 | 150-170 | 1972-1974 | B.B.S. |

*Black cat 1897. Matt on the left and gloss on the right.*

| Model No | Name of Model | Height inches | Current Value £ | US$ | Production Period | Back-stamp |
|---|---|---|---|---|---|---|
| 1200/2 | Mrs Rabbit | 4¼ | 30-35 | 60-70 | 1974-1987 | B.B.S. |
| | (brolly flush to body) | | 30-35 | 60-70 | 1988-1989 | J.B.S. |
| | | | 15·95 | RRP | 1989-C | R.A.B. |
| 1274/1 | Flopsy, Mopsy & | 2¾ | 70-80 | 140-160 | 1953-1971 | G.B.S. |
| | Cottontail | | 35-40 | 70-80 | 1972-1983 | B.B.S. |
| | (Thin base with large heads and full bodies) | | | | | |
| 1274/2 | Flopsy, Mopsy & | 2¾ | 30-35 | 60-70 | 1983-1987 | B.B.S. |
| | Cottontail | | 30-35 | 60-70 | 1988-1989 | J.B.S. |
| | (Thick base with small heads | | 40-50 | 80-100 | 1989-only | R.A.G. |
| | and thinner bodies) | | 15·95 | RRP | 1989-C | R.A.B. |
| | Both variations, same height | | | | | |
| 1275 | Miss Moppet | 3 | 60-70 | 120-140 | 1953-1971 | G.B.S. |
| | | | 30-35 | 60-70 | 1972-1987 | B.B.S. |
| | | | 30-35 | 60-70 | 1988-1989 | J.B.S. |
| | | | 15·95 | RRP | 1989-C | R.A.B. |
| 1276 | Johnny Townmouse | 3½ | 60-70 | 120-140 | 1953-1971 | G.B.S. |
| | | | 30-35 | 60-70 | 1972-1987 | B.B.S. |
| | | | 30-35 | 60-70 | 1988-1989 | J.B.S. |
| | | | 25-30 | 50-60 | 1989-1993 | R.A.B. |
| 1277 | Foxy Whiskered Gentleman | 5 | 70-80 | 140-160 | 1953-1971 | G.B.S. |
| | | | 35-40 | 70-80 | 1972-1987 | B.B.S. |
| | | | 35-40 | 70-80 | 1988-1989 | J.B.S. |
| | | | 15·95 | RRP | 1989-C | R.A.B. |
| 1348/1 | Tommy Brock | 3½ | 150-175 | 300-350 | 1955-1971 | G.B.S. |
| | (spade handle above hand) | | 75-85 | 150-170 | 1972-1974 | B.B.S. |
| 1348/2 | Tommy Brock | 3½ | 30-35 | 60-70 | 1974-1987 | B.B.S. |
| | (spade handle flush with hand) | | 30-35 | 60-70 | 1988-1989 | J.B.S. |
| | | | 15·95 | RRP | 1989-C | R.A.B. |
| 1355 | Duchess, with flowers | 3¾ | 1200-1500 | 2400-3000 | 1955-1967 | G.B.S. |
| 1365/1 | Pigling Bland | 4¼ | 200-250 | 400-500 | 1955-1971 | G.B.S. |
| | (dark mauve jacket and | | 125-150 | 250-300 | 1972-1974 | B.B.S. |
| | 1⅝ in dia base) | | | | | |
| 1365/2 | Pigling Bland | 4¼ | 30-35 | 60-70 | 1974-1987 | B.B.S. |
| | (pale violet jacket and 1⅞ in dia base) | | 30-35 | 60-70 | 1988-1989 | J.B.S. |
| | | | 15·95 | RRP | 1989-C | R.A.B. |
| 1545 | Old Woman Who Lived | 2½ | 60-70 | 120-140 | 1958-1971 | G.B.S. |
| | in a Shoe | | 30-35 | 60-70 | 1972-1987 | B.B.S. |
| | | | 30-35 | 60-70 | 1988-1989 | J.B.S. |
| | | | 15·95 | RRP | 1989-C | R.A.B. |
| 1675 | Goody Tiptoes | 3½ | 60-70 | 120-140 | 1960-1971 | G.B.S. |
| | | | 30-35 | 60-70 | 1972-1987 | B.B.S. |
| | | | 30-35 | 60-70 | 1988-1989 | J.B.S. |
| | | | 15·95 | RRP | 1989-C | R.A.B. |
| 1676/1 | Tabitha Twitchett | 3½ | 80-100 | 160-200 | 1960-1971 | G.B.S. |
| | (blue striped 'V' neck) | | 40-50 | 80-100 | 1972-1974 | B.B.S. |
| 1676/2 | Tabitha Twitchett | 3½ | 30-35 | 60-70 | 1974-1987 | B.B.S. |
| | (white 'V' neck) | | 30-35 | 60-70 | 1988-1989 | J.B.S. |
| | | | 25-30 | 50-60 | 1989-1995 | R.A.B. |
| 1796 | Old Mr Brown | 3¼ | 60-70 | 120-140 | 1962-1971 | G.B.S. |
| | | | 30-35 | 60-70 | 1972-1987 | B.B.S. |
| | | | 30-35 | 60-70 | 1988-1989 | J.B.S. |
| | | | 15·95 | RRP | 1989-C | R.A.B. |
| 1851 | Anna Maria | 3 | 200-250 | 400-500 | 1963-1971 | G.B.S. |
| | | | 100-125 | 200-250 | 1972-1983 | B.B.S. |
| 1940/1 | Mr Benjamin Bunny | 4¼ | 200-250 | 400-500 | 1964-1971 | G.B.S. |
| | (left arm & pipe away from body) | | 125-150 | 250-300 | 1972-1974 | B.B.S. |

| Model No | Name of Model | Height inches | Current Value £ | US$ | Production Period | Back-stamp |
|---|---|---|---|---|---|---|
| 1940/2 | Mr Benjamin Bunny | 4¼ | 30-35 | 60-70 | 1974-1987 | B.B.S. |
| | (left arm & pipe moulded into body) | | 30-35 | 60-70 | 1988-1989 | J.B.S. |
| | | | 15·95 | RRP | 1989-C | R.A.B. |
| 1941/1 | Cecily Parsley | 4 | 100-125 | 200-250 | 1964-1971 | G.B.S. |
| | (ears up and head down) | | 50-60 | 100-120 | 1972-1986 | B.B.S. |
| 1941/2 | Cecily Parsley | 4 | 45-50 | 90-100 | 1986-1987 | B.B.S. |
| | (ears back and head up) | | 45-50 | 90-100 | 1988-1989 | J.B.S. |
| | | | 25-30 | 50-60 | 1989-1993 | R.A.B. |
| 1942 | Mrs Flopsy Bunny | 4 | 100-125 | 200-250 | 1964-1971 | G.B.S. |
| | | | 30-35 | 60-70 | 1972-1987 | B.B.S. |
| | | | 30-35 | 60-70 | 1988-1989 | J.B.S. |
| | | | 15·95 | RRP | 1989-C | R.A.B. |
| 2061 | Amiable Guinea Pig | 3½ | 300-350 | 600-700 | 1966-1971 | G.B.S. |
| | | | 175-200 | 350-400 | 1972-1983 | B.B.S. |
| 2276 | Aunt Pettitoes | 3¾ | 150-175 | 300-350 | 1969-1971 | G.B.S. |
| | | | 30-35 | 60-70 | 1972-1987 | B.B.S. |
| | | | 30-35 | 60-70 | 1988-1989 | J.B.S. |
| | | | 25-30 | 50-60 | 1989-1993 | R.A.B. |
| 2284 | Cousin Ribby | 3¼ | 150-175 | 300-350 | 1970-1971 | G.B.S. |
| | | | 30-35 | 60-70 | 1972-1987 | B.B.S. |
| | | | 30-35 | 60-70 | 1988-1989 | J.B.S. |
| | | | 25-30 | 50-60 | 1989-1993 | R.A.B. |
| 2333 | Appley Dapply | 3¼ | 350-400 | 700-800 | 1971 only | G.B.S. |
| | | | 30-35 | 60-70 | 1972-1987 | B.B.S. |
| | | | 30-35 | 60-70 | 1988-1989 | J.B.S. |
| | | | 15·95 | RRP | 1989-C | R.A.B. |
| 2334 | Pickles | 4½ | 350-400 | 700-800 | 1971 only | G.B.S. |
| | | | 175-200 | 350-400 | 1972-1982 | B.B.S. |
| 2381 | Pig-Wig | 4 | 350-400 | 700-800 | 1971 only | G.B.S. |
| | | | 175-200 | 350-400 | 1972-1982 | B.B.S. |
| 2424 | Mr Alderman Ptolemy | 3¾ | 50-60 | 100-120 | 1973-1987 | B.B.S. |
| | | | 50-60 | 100-120 | 1988-1989 | J.B.S. |
| | | | 15·95 | RRP | 1989-C | R.A.B. |
| 2425 | Sir Isaac Newton | 3⅞ | 175-200 | 350-400 | 1973-1984 | B.B.S. |
| 2452 | Sally Hennypenny | 4 | 30-40 | 60-80 | 1973-1987 | B.B.S. |
| | | | 30-35 | 60-70 | 1988-1989 | J.B.S. |
| | | | 25-30 | 50-60 | 1989-1993 | R.A.B. |
| 2453/1 | Mr Jackson (Green) | 2¾ | 175-200 | 350-400 | 1973-1976 | B.B.S. |
| 2453/2 | Mr Jackson (Fawn) | 2¾ | 30-35 | 60-70 | 1976-1987 | B.B.S. |
| | | | 30-35 | 60-70 | 1988-1989 | J.B.S. |
| | | | 20-25 | 50-60 | 1989-1997 | R.A.B. |
| 2508 | Simpkin | 4 | 350-400 | 700-800 | 1974-1982 | B.B.S. |
| 2509 | Mr Benjamin Bunny & | 4 | 70-90 | 140-180 | 1974-1987 | B.B.S. |
| | Peter Rabbit | | 70-90 | 140-180 | 1988-1989 | J.B.S. |
| | | | 40-50 | 80-100 | 1989-1995 | R.A.B. |
| 2543 | Mrs Rabbit & Bunnies | 3½ | 35-40 | 70-80 | 1976-1987 | B.B.S. |
| | | | 35-40 | 70-80 | 1988-1989 | J.B.S. |
| | | | 45-50 | 90-100 | 1989 only | R.A.G. |
| | | | 15·95 | RRP | 1989-C | R.A.B. |
| 2544 | Tabitha Twitchett with | 3½ | 70-90 | 140-180 | 1976-1987 | B.B.S. |
| | Miss Moppett | | 70-90 | 140-180 | 1988-1989 | J.B.S. |
| | | | 40-50 | 80-100 | 1989-1993 | R.A.B. |
| 2559 | Ginger | 3¾ | 350-400 | 700-800 | 1976-1982 | B.B.S. |

| Model No | Name of Model | Height inches | Current Value £ | US$ | Production Period | Back-stamp |
|---|---|---|---|---|---|---|
| 2560 | Poorly Peter Rabbit | 3½ | 30-35 | 60-70 | 1976-1987 | B.B.S. |
| | | | 35-40 | 70-80 | 1972-1987 | B.B.S. |
| | | | 30-35 | 60-70 | 1988-1989 | J.B.S. |
| | | | 15·95 | RRP | 1989-C | R.A.B. |
| 2584 | Hunca Munca Sweeping | 3⅛ | 30-35 | 60-70 | 1977-1987 | B.B.S. |
| | | | 30-35 | 60-70 | 1988-1989 | J.B.S. |
| | | | 15·95 | RRP | 1989-C | R.A.B. |
| 2585 | Little Black Rabbit | 4⅜ | 30-35 | 60-70 | 1977-1987 | B.B.S. |
| | | | 30-35 | 60-70 | 1988-1989 | J.B.S. |
| | | | 20-25 | 40-50 | 1989-1997 | R.A.B. |
| 2586/1 | Fierce Bad Rabbit (feet up) | 4¾ | 100-125 | 200-250 | 1977-1980 | B.B.S. |
| 2586/2 | Fierce Bad Rabbit (feet down) | 4¾ | 30-35 | 60-70 | 1980-1987 | B.B.S. |
| | | | 30-35 | 60-70 | 1988-1989 | J.B.S. |
| | | | 15·95 | RRP | 1989-C | R.A.B. |
| 2601 | Duchess, with pie | 4 | 150-200 | 300-400 | 1979-1982 | B.B.S. |
| 2627 | Chippy Hackee | 3¾ | 30-35 | 60-70 | 1980-1987 | B.B.S. |
| | | | 30-35 | 60-70 | 1988-1989 | J.B.S. |
| | | | 25-30 | 50-60 | 1989-1993 | R.A.B. |
| 2628 | Mr Drake Puddleduck | 4¼ | 30-35 | 60-70 | 1980-1987 | B.B.S. |
| | | | 30-35 | 60-70 | 1988-1989 | J.B.S. |
| | | | 15·95 | RRP | 1989-C | R.A.B. |
| 2647 | Rebeccah Puddleduck | 3¼ | 30-35 | 60-70 | 1981-1987 | B.B.S. |
| | | | 30-35 | 60-70 | 1988-1989 | J.B.S. |
| | | | 15·95 | RRP | 1989-C | R.A.B. |
| 2668 | Thomasina Tittlemouse | 3¼ | 50-60 | 100-120 | 1981-1987 | B.B.S. |
| | | | 50-60 | 100-120 | 1988-1989 | J.B.S. |
| | (very small number) | | 100-150 | 200-300 | 1989 only | R.A.B. |
| 2713 | Diggory Diggory Delvet | 2¾ | 30-35 | 60-70 | 1982-1987 | B.B.S. |
| | | | 30-35 | 60-70 | 1988-1989 | J.B.S. |
| | | | 15·95 | RRP | 1989-C | R.A.B. |
| 2716 | Susan | 4½ | 125-150 | 250-300 | 1983-1987 | B.B.S. |
| | | | 125-150 | 250-300 | 1988-1989 | J.B.S. |
| | (very small number) | | 150-175 | 300-350 | 1989 only | R.A.B. |
| 2767 | Old Mr Pricklepin | 2½ | 50-60 | 100-120 | 1983-1987 | B.B.S. |
| | | | 50-60 | 100-120 | 1988-1989 | J.B.S. |
| | (very small number) | | 100-150 | 40-50 | 1989 only | R.A.B. |
| 2803/1 | Benjamin Bunny sat on a Bank (head to side) | 3¾ | 60-70 | 120-140 | 1983-1986 | B.B.S. |
| 2803/2 | Benjamin Bunny sat on a Bank (head to front) | 3¾ | 30-35 | 60-70 | 1986-1987 | B.B.S. |
| | | | 30-35 | 60-70 | 1988-1989 | J.B.S. |
| | | | 15·95 | RRP | 1989-C | R.A.B. |
| 2804 | Old Woman Who Lived in a Shoe – knitting | 3 | 125-150 | 250-300 | 1983-1987 | B.B.S. |
| | | | 125-150 | 250-300 | 1988-1989 | J.B.S. |
| | | | 15·95 | RRP | 1989-C | R.A.B. |
| 2823 | Jemima Puddleduck made a Feather Nest | 2¼ | 30-35 | 60-70 | 1983-1987 | B.B.S. |
| | | | 30-35 | 60-70 | 1988-1989 | J.B.S. |
| | | | 20-25 | 40-50 | 1989-1997 | R.A.B. |
| 2877 | Mrs Tiggy-Winkle takes Tea | 3¼ | 125-150 | 250-300 | 1985-1987 | B.B.S. |
| | | | 125-150 | 250-300 | 1988-1989 | J.B.S. |
| | | | 15·95 | RRP | 1989-C | R.A.B. |
| 2878 | Cottontail | 3½ | 30-35 | 60-70 | 1985-1987 | B.B.S. |
| | | | 30-35 | 60-70 | 1988-1989 | J.B.S. |
| | | | 25-30 | 50-60 | 1989-1996 | R.A.B. |
| 2956 | Old Mr Bouncer | 2⅞ | 50-75 | 100-150 | 1986-1987 | B.B.S. |
| | | | 50-75 | 100-150 | 1988-1989 | J.B.S. |
| | | | 25-30 | 50-60 | 1989-1995 | R.A.B. |

| Model No | Name of Model | Height inches | Current Value £ | US$ | Production Period | Back-stamp |
|---|---|---|---|---|---|---|
| 2957 | Goody and Timmy Tiptoes | 4 | 125-150 | 250-300 | 1986-1987 | B.B.S. |
| | | | 125-150 | 250-300 | 1988-1989 | J.B.S. |
| | | | 40-50 | 80-100 | 1989-1996 | R.A.B. |
| 2965 | John Joiner (Dog) | 2½ | 15·95 | RRP | 1990-C | R.A.B. |
| 2966 | Mother Ladybird | 2½ | 30-35 | 60-70 | 1989-1996 | R.A.B. |
| 2971 | Babbitty Bumble (Bee) | 2¾ | 50-60 | 100-120 | 1989-1993 | R.A.B. |
| 2989 | Tom Thumb | 3 | 100-125 | 200-250 | 1988 only | B.B.S. |
| | | | 100-125 | 200-250 | 1988-1989 | J.B.S. |
| | | | 20-25 | 40-50 | 1989-1997 | R.A.B. |
| 2996 | Timmy Willie sleeping | 1¾ | 100-125 | 200-250 | 1987 only | B.B.S. |
| | | | 100-125 | 200-250 | 1988-1989 | J.B.S. |
| | | | 25-30 | 50-60 | 1989-1996 | R.A.B. |
| 3030 | Tom Kitten & Butterfly | 3½ | 125-150 | 250-300 | 1987 only | B.B.S. |
| | | | 125-150 | 250-300 | 1988-1989 | J.B.S. |
| | | | 50-60 | 100-120 | 1989-1994 | R.A.B. |
| 3031 | Little Pig Robinson spying | 3½ | 125-150 | 250-300 | 1987 only | B.B.S. |
| | | | 125-150 | 250-300 | 1988-1989 | J.B.S. |
| | | | 50-75 | 100-150 | 1989-1993 | R.A.B. |
| 3090 | Mr Jeremy Fisher digging | 3½ | 125-150 | 250-300 | 1988-1989 | J.B.S. |
| | | | 50-75 | 100-150 | 1989-1994 | R.A.B. |
| 3091 | Mr Tod | 4¾ | 175-200 | 350-400 | 1988-1989 | J.B.S. |
| | | | 50-75 | 100-150 | 1989-1993 | R.A.B. |
| 3094 | Johnny Townmouse with bag | 3½ | 125-150 | 250-300 | 1988-1989 | J.B.S. |
| | | | 50-75 | 100-150 | 1989-1994 | R.A.B. |
| 3157 | Peter in the Gooseberry Net | 2 | 40-50 | 80-100 | 1990-1995 | R.A.B. |
| 3193 | Jemima Puddleduck with Foxy Whiskered Gentleman | 4¾ | 25·95 | RRP | 1990-C | R.A.B. |
| 3197 | Mittens & Moppet | 3¾ | 50-75 | 100-150 | 1990-1994 | R.A.B. |
| 3200 | Gentleman Mouse made a Bow | 3 | 25-30 | 50-60 | 1990-1996 | R.A.B. |
| 3219 | Foxy Reading Country News | 4¼ | 30-40 | 60-70 | 1990-1997 | R.A.B. |
| 3220 | Lady Mouse Made a Curtsy | 2¾ | 15·95 | RRP | 1990-C | R.A.B. |
| 3234 | Benjamin Wakes Up | 2¼ | 15·95 | RRP | 1991-C | R.A.B. |
| 3242 | Peter and the Red Pocket Handkerchief | 4½ | 16·95 | RRP | 1991-C | R.A.B. |
| 3251 | Miss Dormouse | 4 | 50-75 | 100-150 | 1991-1995 | R.A.B. |
| 3252 | Pigling Eats His Porridge | 4 | 50-60 | 100-120 | 1991-1994 | R.A.B. |
| 3257 | Christmas Stocking (Hunca Munca & Wife) | 3½ | 50-75 | 100-150 | 1991-1994 | R.A.B. |
| 3278 | Mrs Rabbit Cooking | 4 | 15·95 | RRP | 1992-C | R.A.B. |
| 3280 | Ribby and the Patty Pan | 3½ | 15·95 | RRP | 1992-C | R.A.B. |
| 3288 | Hunca Munca Spills the Beads | 3¼ | 25-30 | 50-60 | 1992-1996 | R.A.B. |
| 3317 | Benjamin Bunny Eats a Lettuce Leaf | 4¾ | 15.95 | RRP | 1992-C | R.A.B. |
| 3319 | And This Little Pig Had None | 3½ | 15.95 | RRP | 1992-C | R.A.B. |
| 3325 | No More Twist | 3⅝ | 25-30 | 50-60 | 1992-1997 | R.A.B. |
| 3356 | Peter Rabbit (large size) | 6¾ | 50-60 | 100-120 | 1993 only | B.B.P.R |
| | | | 28·95 | RRP | 1994-C | R.A.B. |
| 3372 | Jeremy Fisher (large size) | 5 | 28·95 | RRP | 1994-C | R.A.B. |
| 3373 | Jemima Puddleduck (large size) | 6¼ | 50-60 | 100-120 | 1994 only | G.B.J.P. |
| | | | 28·95 | RRP | 1995-C | R.A.B. |
| 3398 | Mrs Rabbit (large size) | 6 | 28·95 | RRP | 1994-C | R.A.B. |
| 3403 | Benjamin Bunny (large size) | 6 | 28·95 | RRP | 1994-C | R.A.B. |
| 3405 | Tom Kitten (large size) | 5¼ | 28·95 | RRP | 1994-C | R.A.B. |
| 3437 | Mrs Tiggy-Winkle (large size) | 4½ | 28·95 | RRP | 1997-C | R.A.B. |

| Model No | Name of Model | Height inches | Current Value £ | US$ | Production Period | Back-stamp |
|---|---|---|---|---|---|---|
| 3449 | The Tailor of Gloucester (large size) | 7¼ | 28·95 | RRP | 1995-C | R.A.B. |
| 3450 | Foxy Whiskered Gentleman (large size) | 7 | 28·95 | RRP | 1995-C | R.A.B. |
| 3473 | Peter in Bed | 2¾ | 19·95 | RRP | 1995-C | R.A.B. |
| 3506 | Mr McGregor | 5¼ | 18·95 | RRP | 1995-C | R.A.B. |
| 3533 | Peter Ate a Radish | 4 | 17·95 | RRP | 1995-C | R.A.B. |
| 3591 | Peter Rabbit with Postbag | 4¾ | 18·95 | RRP | 1996-C | R.A.B. |
| 3592 | Peter Rabbit with Handkerchief (large size) | 7¼ | 28·95 | RRP | 1996-C | R.A.B. |
| 3597 | Peter Rabbit with Daffodils | 4¾ | 18·95 | RRP | 1996-C | R.A.B. |
| 3646 | Mrs Rabbit & Peter | 3½ | 27·95 | RRP | 1997-C | R.A.B. |
| 3672 | Mrs Rabbit & the Four Bunnies (on wood base) | 4¼ | 99·95 | RRP | 1997 only | † |

†*Special Beswick backstamp to celebrate the 50th Anniversary of making Beatrix Potter figures at the Beswick factory. Edition of 1997, together with a Certificate.*

## Beatrix Potter – Wall Plaques, stand and Tree lamp base

| Model No | Name of Model | Height inches | Current Value £ | US$ | Production Period | Back-stamp |
|---|---|---|---|---|---|---|
| 1531 | Tree lamp base | 7 | 65-75 | 130-150 | 1958-1982 | B.B.S. |
| 2082 | Jemima Puddleduck (plaque) | 6 | 1500-2000 | 3000-4000 | 1967-1969 | G.B.S. |
| 2083 | Peter Rabbit (plaque) | 6 | 1500-2000 | 3000-4000 | 1967-1969 | G.B.S. |
| 2085 | Tom Kitten (plaque) | 6 | 1500-2000 | 3000-4000 | 1967-1969 | G.B.S. |
| 2295 | Tree Trunks Display Stand | 12½ x2½ | 25-30 | 50-60 | 1970-1989 | B.B.S.‡ |
| 2594 | Jemima Puddleduck & Foxy Whiskered Gentleman (plaque) – 1st edition | 7½ x7½ | 80-100 | 160-200 | 1977-1982 | B.B.S. |
| 2650 | Peter Rabbit (plaque) – 2nd edition | 7½ x7½ | 80-100 | 160-200 | 1979-1982 | B.B.S. |

*Leopard **841**, quite a rare piece.*

| Model No | Name of Model | Height inches | Current Value £ | US$ | Production Period | Back- stamp |
|---|---|---|---|---|---|---|
| 2685 | Mrs Tittlemouse (plaque) – 3rd edition | 7½x7½ | 100-120 | 200-240 | 1981-1982 | B.B.S. |

‡ *also currently found with a Royal Albert or Royal Doulton backstamp at £19·95. Discontinued June 1997.*

## Beatrix Potter – Character Jugs

| Model No | Name of Model | Height inches | Current Value £ | US$ | Production Period | Back- stamp |
|---|---|---|---|---|---|---|
| 2959 | Old Mr Brown | 2½ | 50-60 | 100-120 | 1987-1989 | J.B.S. |
|  |  |  | 60-70 | 120-140 | 1989-1992 | R.A.B. |
| 2960 | Jeremy Fisher | 2¾ | 50-60 | 100-120 | 1987-1989 | J.B.S. |
|  |  |  | 60-70 | 120-140 | 1989-1992 | R.A.B. |
| 3006 | Peter Rabbit | 2¾ | 50-60 | 100-120 | 1987-1989 | J.B.S. |
|  |  |  | 60-70 | 120-140 | 1989-1992 | R.A.B. |
| 3088 | Jemima Puddleduck | 3¼ | 60-70 | 120-140 | 1988-1989 | J.B.S. |
|  |  |  | 70-80 | 140-160 | 1989-1992 | R.A.B. |
| 3102 | Mrs Tiggle-Winkle | 3 | 60-70 | 120-140 | 1988-1989 | J.B.S. |
|  |  |  | 70-80 | 140-160 | 1989-1992 | R.A.B. |
| 3103 | Tom Kitten | 3 | 60-70 | 120-140 | 1988-1989 | J.B.S. |
|  |  |  | 70-80 | 140-160 | 1989-1992 | R.A.B. |

*There were a much smaller number of Royal Albert marked jugs, than John Beswick.*

## Beatrix Potter boxed sets

These sets consist of a transparent window box containing a copy of one of the 'little books' by Beatrix Potter, together with the relevant model. All were available with either Beswick or Royal Albert backstamps

| Model No | Name of Book and Model | Current Value Beswick £ | US$ | R Albert £ | US$ | Production Period |
|---|---|---|---|---|---|---|
| 1092/2 | Jemima Puddleduck | 35 | RRP | 23·50 | RRP | 1/86-C |
| 1098/2 | Peter Rabbit | 35 | RRP | 23·50 | RRP | 1/86-C |
| 1100 | Tom Kitten | 35 | 70 | 25 | 50 | 8/87-12/92 |
| 1101 | Timmy Tiptoes | 35 | 70 | 25 | 50 | 8/88-12/92 |
| 1102 | Squirrel Nutkin | 35 | 70 | 25 | 50 | 1/90-12/92 |
| 1103 | Mrs Tittlemouse | 35 | 70 | 25 | 50 | 8/88-12/92 |
| 1105/3 | Benjamin Bunny | 35 | RRP | 23·50 | RRP | 1/86-C |
| 1106 | Samuel Whiskers | 35 | 70 | 25 | 50 | 1/90-12/92 |
| 1107/2 | Mrs Tiggy-Winkle | 35 | RRP | 23·50 | RRP | 1/86-C |
| 1108 | Tailor of Gloucester | 35 | 70 | 25 | 50 | 8/87-12/92 |
| 1157/2 | Jeremy Fisher | 35 | 70 | 25 | 50 | 8/87-12/92 |
| 1275 | Miss Moppet | 35 | 70 | 25 | 50 | 8/88-12/92 |
| 1276 | Johnny Townmouse | 35 | 70 | 25 | 50 | 1/90-12/92 |
| 2333 | Appley Dapply | 35 | 70 | 25 | RRP | 8/87-12/92 |
| 2586/2 | Fierce Bad Rabbit | 35 | 70 | 25 | 50 | 8/88-12/92 |

## Snow White and the Seven Dwarfs Figures

All models carry the G.B.S. gold backstamp

| Model No | Name of Model | Height inches | Current Value £ | US$ | Production Period |
|---|---|---|---|---|---|
| 1325 | Dopey | 3½ | 125-175 | 250-350 | 1954-1967 |
| 1326 | Happy | 3½ | 125-175 | 250-350 | 1954-1967 |
| 1327 | Bashful | 3½ | 125-175 | 250-350 | 1954-1967 |
| 1328 | Sneezy | 3½ | 125-175 | 250-350 | 1954-1967 |
| 1329 | Doc | 3½ | 125-175 | 250-350 | 1954-1967 |

| Model No | Name of Model | Height inches | Current Value £ | US$ | Production Period |
|---|---|---|---|---|---|
| 1330 | Grumpy | 3½ | 125-175 | 250-350 | 1954-1967 |
| 1331 | Sleepy | 3½ | 125-175 | 250-350 | 1954-1967 |
| 1332/1 | Snow White (face looking straight ahead) | 5 | 400-500 | 800-1000 | 1954 only |
| 1332/2 | Snow White (face turned and looking up) | 5 | 350-400 | 700-800 | 1955-1967 |

## Winnie the Pooh Figures – First series
Early models of the first six shapes carry a G.B.S. gold backstamp.

| Model No | Name of Model | Height inches | Current Value £ | US$ | Production Period |
|---|---|---|---|---|---|
| 2193 | Winnie the Pooh | 2½ | 60-80 | 80-90 | 1969-1989 |
| 2196 | Eeyore | 2 | 50-60 | 100-120 | 1969-1989 |
| 2214 | Piglet | 2¾ | 50-60 | 100-120 | 1969-1989 |
| 2215 | Rabbit | 3⅛ | 50-60 | 100-120 | 1969-1989 |
| 2216 | Owl | 3 | 50-60 | 100-120 | 1969-1989 |
| 2217 | Kanga | 3⅛ | 50-60 | 100-120 | 1969-1989 |
| 2394 | Tigger | 3 | 100-125 | 200-250 | 1972-1989 |
| 2395 | Christopher Robin | 4¾ | 100-125 | 200-250 | 1972-1989 |

## Alice in Wonderland Figures

| Model No | Name of Model | Height inches | Current Value £ | US$ | Production Period |
|---|---|---|---|---|---|
| 2476 | Alice | 4¾ | 200-250 | 400-500 | 1975-1981 |
| 2477 | White Rabbit | 4¾ | 200-250 | 400-500 | 1975-1981 |
| 2478 | Mock Turtle | 4¼ | 75-100 | 150-200 | 1975-1981 |
| 2479 | Mad Hatter | 4¼ | 175-200 | 350-400 | 1975-1981 |
| ‡2480 | Cheshire Cat | 1½ | 300-400 | 600-800 | 1975-1981 |
| 2485 | Gryphon | 3¼ | 75-100 | 150-200 | 1975-1981 |
| 2489 | King of Hearts | 3¾ | 60-70 | 120-140 | 1975-1981 |
| 2490 | Queen of Hearts | 4 | 60-70 | 120-140 | 1975-1981 |
| 2545 | Dodo | 4 | 125-150 | 250-300 | 1976-1981 |
| 2546 | Fish Footman | 4⅝ | 150-200 | 300-400 | 1976-1981 |
| 2547 | Frog Footman | 4¼ | 200-250 | 400-500 | 1976-1981 |

‡also with "Swiss-Roll" decoration

## Rupert Bear Figures

| Model No | Name of Model | Height inches | Current Value £ | US$ | Production Period |
|---|---|---|---|---|---|
| 2694 | Rupert Bear | 4¼ | 225-275 | 360-450 | 1982-1985 |
| 2710 | Algy Pug | 4 | 125-150 | 250-300 | 1982-1985 |
| 2711 | Pong Ping | 4¼ | 125-150 | 250-300 | 1982-1985 |
| 2720 | Bill Badger | 2¾ | 125-150 | 250-300 | 1982-1985 |
| 2779 | Rupert Bear snowballing | 4¼ | 275-325 | 550-650 | 1983-1985 |

## Kitty MacBride Figures

| Model No | Name of Model | Height inches | Current Value £ | US$ | Production Period |
|---|---|---|---|---|---|
| 2526 | A Family Mouse | 3⅜ | 60-80 | 120-160 | 1975-1983 |
| 2527 | A Double Act | 3⅜ | 60-80 | 120-160 | 1975-1983 |
| 2528 | The Racegoer | 3⅜ | 40-60 | 80-120 | 1975-1983 |
| 2529 | A Good Read | 2⅝ | 200-250 | 400-500 | 1975-1983 |
| 2530 | Lazy Bones | 1⅝ | 60-80 | 120-160 | 1975-1983 |
| 2531 | A Snack | 3¼ | 40-60 | 80-120 | 1975-1983 |
| 2532 | Strained Relations | 3⅛ | 40-60 | 80-120 | 1975-1983 |
| 2533 | Just Good Friends | 3⅛ | 60-80 | 120-160 | 1975-1983 |
| 2565 | The Ring | 3¼ | 60-80 | 120-160 | 1976-1983 |
| 2566 | Guilty Sweethearts | 2¼ | 60-80 | 120-160 | 1976-1983 |
| 2589 | All I Do Is Think of You | 2⅜ | 225-275 | 250-350 | 1977-1983 |

## Walt Disney Character Figures

All backstamps are gold.

| Model No | Name of Model | Height inches | Current Value £ | US$ | Production Period |
|---|---|---|---|---|---|
| 1278 | Mickey Mouse | 3⅞ | 400-500 | 800-1000 | 1954-1965 |
| 1279 | Jiminy Cricket | 4 | 400-500 | 800-1000 | 1954-1965 |
| 1280 | Pluto | 3½ | 400-500 | 800-1000 | 1954-1965 |
| 1281 | Goofy | 4¼ | 400-500 | 800-1000 | 1954-1965 |
| 1282 | Pinocchio | 4 | 400-500 | 800-1000 | 1954-1965 |
| 1283 | Donald Duck | 4 | 400-500 | 800-1000 | 1954-1965 |
| 1289 | Minnie Mouse | 4 | 400-500 | 800-1000 | 1954-1965 |
| 1291 | Thumper | 3¾ | 400-500 | 800-1000 | 1954-1965 |
| 1301 | Nana | 3¼ | 400-500 | 800-1000 | 1954-1965 |
| 1302 | Smee | 4⅛ | 400-500 | 800-1000 | 1954-1965 |
| 1307 | Peter Pan | 5 | 400-500 | 800-1000 | 1954-1965 |
| 1312 | Tinkerbell | 5 | 400-500 | 800-1000 | 1954-1965 |

## Wind in the Willows Figures

Only available with a Royal Albert Backstamp

| Model No | Name of Model | Height inches | Current Value £ | US$ | Production Period |
|---|---|---|---|---|---|
| 2939 | Mole — AW4 | 3 | 30-40 | 60-80 | 1987-1989 |
| 2940 | Badger — AW3 | 3 | 30-40 | 60-80 | 1987-1989 |
| 2941 | Ratty— AW2 | 3⅝ | 30-40 | 60-80 | 1987-1989 |
| 2942 | Toad — AW1 | 3⅝ | 30-40 | 60-80 | 1987-1989 |
| 3065 | Portly (Otter) AW6 | 2¾ | 125-175 | 150-350 | 1988-1989 |
| 3076 | Weasel Gamekeeper AW5 | 4 | 125-175 | 150-350 | 1988-1989 |

## Thelwell Figures

| Model No | Name of Model | Height inches | Current Value £ | US$ | Production Period |
|---|---|---|---|---|---|
| 2704 | An Angel on Horseback | 4½ | 80-100 | 160-200 | 1982-1989 |
| 2769 | Kick Start | 3½ | 80-100 | 160-200 | 1983-1989 |
| 2789 | Pony Express | 4½ | 80-100 | 160-200 | 1983-1989 |

*All three available in Bay or Grey*

## David Hand Animal Land Figures

All backstamps are gold

| Model No | Name of Model | Height inches | Current Value £ | US$ | Production Period |
|---|---|---|---|---|---|
| 1148 | Dinkum Platypus | 4¼ | 200-250 | 400-500 | 1950-1955 |
| 1150 | Zimmy Lion | 3¾ | 400-500 | 800-1000 | 1950-1955 |
| 1151 | Felia Cat | 4 | 400-500 | 800-1000 | 1950-1955 |
| 1152 | Ginger Nutt | 4 | 200-250 | 400-500 | 1950-1955 |
| 1153 | Hazel Nutt | 3¾ | 200-250 | 400-500 | 1950-1955 |
| 1154 | Oscar Ostrich (Olly) | 3¾ | 400-500 | 800-1000 | 1950-1955 |
| 1155 | Dusty Mole | 3½ | 200-250 | 400-500 | 1950-1955 |
| 1156 | Loopy Hare | 4¼ | 400-500 | 800-1000 | 1950-1955 |

## Remainder not in categories

| Model No | Name of Model | Height inches | Current Value £ | US$ | Production Period |
|---|---|---|---|---|---|
| 857 | Alice & White Rabbit (on base) | — | 90-100 | 180-200 | 1940-1950 |
| 858 | Dormouse & Alice (plaque) | — | 90-100 | 180-200 | 1940-1950 |
| 859 | King & Alice (plaque) | — | 90-100 | 180-200 | 1940-1950 |
| 860 | Alice playing croquet (on base) | — | 90-100 | 180-200 | 1940-1950 |
| 861 | Cinderella feeding birds (plaque) | — | 90-100 | 180-200 | 1940-1950 |
| 863 | Cinderella dressing the ugly sisters (plaque) | — | 90-100 | 180-200 | 1940-1950 |
| 865 | Cinderella running from the ball (plaque) | — | 90-100 | 180-200 | 1940-1950 |
| 866 | Dandini with Trumpet & slipper (plaque) | — | 90-100 | 180-200 | 1940-1950 |
| 867 | The Prince finds Cinderella (plaque) | — | 90-100 | 180-200 | 1940-1950 |

# Comical Animals and Birds – Novelties

(All models carry a Beswick backstamp)

Apart from their modelling skills many of the Beswick artists have had another strong asset, a lively sense of humour, and this is reflected in a large number of pieces in the collection. A time-honoured way of raising a smile is to endow an animal with human characteristics, and so it is not surprising to find dogs, cats and monkeys playing musical instruments, a cat hiking, a duck on skis, penguins sporting umbrellas and even a monkey smoking a pipe, one of the most appealing studies in the group. Sometimes facial expressions alone are sufficient to amuse, as with the dog going cross-eyed looking at a ladybird on the end of his nose (804). Occasionally the animals themselves join in the joke — there are laughing pigs, cats and a dog introduced in 1967.

Frequently the Beswick artists have sought comedy in familiar situations such as the cats curled up on chimney pots which form a cruet set in the 'Fun Ceramics' collection or the snoozing pigs in the 'Farmyard Humour' series. More recently the 'Little Loveable' Clown Series were introduced, together with the 'English Country Folk' and 'Pig Prom' series. These are listed separately later in the book.

The ability to entertain in this way is an endearing aspect of the Beswick story and hopefully the laughter will continue for many years to come.

| Model No | Name of Model | Height inches | Current Value £ | US$ | Production Period |
|---|---|---|---|---|---|
| 317 | Duck on base | 8¼ | 100-150 | 200-300 | 1936-1954 |
| 324 | Poodle begging | 7 | 100-150 | 200-300 | 1936-1954 |
| 624 | Rabbit with knapsack | 4 | 75-100 | 150-200 | 1938-1954 |
| 663 | Elephant with five ton weight (spill holder) | — | 50-60 | 100-120 | 1938-1954 |
| 664 | Fox with elbow on tree trunk (spill holder) | 4½ | 75-100 | 150-200 | 1938-1954 |
| 665 | Rabbit with golf bag (spill holder) | 4¾ | 75-100 | 150-200 | 1938-1954 |
| 688 | Teddy bear | — | 75-100 | 150-200 | 1939-1954 |
| 697 | Hippo Laughing | 2¼ | 50-75 | 100-150 | 1939-1954 |
| 698/1 | Giraffe (large) | — | 60-80 | 120-160 | 1939-1954 |
| 698/2 | Giraffe (medium) | — | 55-75 | 110-150 | 1939-1954 |
| 698/3 | Giraffe (small) | — | 50-70 | 100-140 | 1940-1954 |
| 760 | Duck with ladybird on nose | 3⅞ | 20-30 | 40-60 | 1939-1971 |
| 761 | Dog with bandage | 4¼ | 50-60 | 100-120 | 1939-1971 |
| 762 | Duck on skis | 3¼ | 40-50 | 80-100 | 1939-1969 |
| 765 | Three Ducks | 2¾ | 30-40 | 60-80 | 1939-1971 |
| 802/1 | Penguin with orange umbrella up | 4¼ | 40-60 | 80-120 | 1940-1956 |
| 802/2 | Penguin with red umbrella up | 4¼ | 30-35 | 60-70 | 1956-1972 |
| 803 | Penguin with walking stick (Part of set see 800 and 801 in Birds) | 3¾ | 25-30 | 50-60 | 1940-1972 |
| 804 | Dog with ladybird on nose | 4 | 20-25 | 40-50 | 1940-1969 |
| 805/1 | Dog with ladybird on tail | 3¾ | 20-25 | 40-50 | 1940-1969 |
| 805/2 | Dog with ladybird on tail | 2½ | 15-20 | 30-40 | 1940-1969 |
| 811 | Dog playing accordian | 4 | 50-75 | 100-150 | 1940-1961 |
| 812 | Dog asleep on drum | 2⅞ | 40-60 | 80-120 | 1940-1961 |
| 813 | Dog with ladybird on nose | 4 | 20-30 | 40-60 | 1940-1967 |
| 831 | Dog with glasses reading book | 6¼ | 75-100 | 150-200 | 1940-1961 |
| 907 | Dog with ladybird on tail | 3¼ | 20-25 | 40-50 | 1941-1971 |
| 1001 | Cockerel | 5¾ | 200-250 | 400-500 | 1945-1961 |
| 1002 | Puppit dog | 4¾ | 35-45 | 70-90 | 1945-1969 |
| 1003 | Fawnie | 5¼ | 175-225 | 350-450 | 1945-1967 |
| 1004 | Rooster | 7 | 200-250 | 400-500 | 1945-1961 |
| 1005 | Kangarinie | 5 | 200-250 | 400-500 | 1945-1961 |
| 1006 | Grebie (small duck) | 5¼ | 250-300 | 500-600 | 1945-1954 |
| 1026 | Cat orchestra conductor | 2 | 25-35 | 50-70 | 1945-1972 |
| 1027 | Cat cellist | 2 | 25-35 | 50-70 | 1945-1972 |
| 1028 | Cat violinist | 2 | 25-35 | 50-70 | 1945-1972 |
| 1029 | Cat saxophonist | 2 | 25-35 | 50-70 | 1945-1972 |
| 1049 | Monkey smoking pipe | 4¼ | 60-80 | 120-160 | 1946-1968 |
| 1054 | Dog holding 'My Plate' | 4¼ | 50-60 | 100-120 | 1947-1967 |
| 1058 | Dog | 4½ | 35-45 | 70-90 | 1946-1967 |
| 1088 | Dog | 3½ | 35-45 | 70-90 | 1947-1968 |
| 1099 | Cock and Hen (set of 2) Salt & Pepper | 1¾ | 30-50 | 60-100 | 1947-1962 |
| 1255 | Monkey drummer | 2⅝ | 100-125 | 200-250 | 1952-1962 |
| 1256 | Monkey tuba player | 2⅝ | 100-125 | 200-250 | 1952-1962 |
| 1257 | Monkey fiddler | 2⅝ | 100-125 | 200-250 | 1952-1962 |
| 1258 | Monkey saxophonist | 2⅝ | 100-125 | 200-250 | 1952-1962 |
| 1259 | Monkey guitarist | 2⅝ | 100-125 | 200-250 | 1952-1962 |
| 1260 | Monkey banjo player | 2⅝ | 100-125 | 200-250 | 1952-1962 |
| 1335 | Tortoise mother | 2¾ long | 50-60 | 100-120 | 1954-1972 |
| 1336 | Tortoise girl | 1¾ long | 30-40 | 60-80 | 1954-1972 |
| 1337 | Tortoise boy | 1¾ long | 30-40 | 60-80 | 1954-1972 |
| 1379 | Bush Baby with mirror | 2 | 50-75 | 100-150 | 1955-1965 |
| 1380 | Bush Baby with stud | 2 | 50-75 | 100-150 | 1955-1965 |

| Model No | Name of Model | Height inches | Current Value £ | US$ | Production Period |
|---|---|---|---|---|---|
| 1381 | Bush Baby with candy | 1½ | 50-75 | 100-150 | 1955-1965 |
| 1733 | Fox (sitting) | 3¾ | 50-60 | 100-120 | 1962-1968 |
| 1738 | Pup with bone | 3¾ | 60-75 | 120-150 | 1962-1967 |
| 2100 | Cat and mouse laughing | 3 | 60-80 | 120-160 | 1967-1972 |
| 2101 | Cat laughing | 3 | 40-50 | 80-100 | 1967-1972 |
| 2102 | Dog laughing | 2⅞ | 40-50 | 80-100 | 1967-1972 |
| 2103 | Two Pigs laughing | 2¾ | 60-80 | 120-160 | 1967-1971 |
| 2130 | Dog praying | 2⅞ | 40-50 | 80-100 | 1967-1972 |
| 2131 | Rabbit yawning | 2⅞ | 40-50 | 80-100 | 1967-1972 |
| 2132 | Rabbit & baby asleep | 2⅞ | 60-80 | 120-160 | 1967-1971 |
| 2200 | Chicken running | 1¼ | 30-35 | 60-70 | 1968-1973 |
| 2201 | Chicken pecking | 1 | 30-35 | 60-70 | 1968-1973 |
| 2202 | Chicken sitting | 1½ | 30-35 | 60-70 | 1968-1973 |
| 2746 | Pig & piglet riding piggy back | 2¾ | 30-35 | 60-70 | 1981-1994 |
| 2761 | Cat asleep on chimney. Salt, pepper and stand | 4 | 50-75 | 100-150 | 1982-1986 |
| †2792 | Daisy the Cow creamer | 5¾ | 40-50 | 80-100 | 1983-1989 |
| 2802 | Umbrella money box "Saving for a Rainy Day" | 5¼ | 40-50 | 80-100 | 1983-1986 |
| 2805 | Pillar Box money box with cat on top | 6¼ | 40-50 | 80-100 | 1983-1986 |
| 2810 | Egg cup with cat | 2⅜ | 25-30 | 50-60 | 1983-1986 |
| *3012 | Sporting Cat Footballer in striped colours | 4⅛ | 35-45 | 70-90 | 1987 only |
| A | Orange and White | | | | |
| B | Maroon and White | | | | |
| C | Black and White | | | | |
| D | Light Blue and White | | | | |
| E | Yellow & White | | | | |
| *3016 | Sporting Cat Footballer in plain colours | 4⅛ | 35-45 | 70-90 | 1987 only |
| A | Orange and White | | | | |
| B | Maroon and White | | | | |
| C | Black and White | | | | |
| D | Light Blue and White | | | | |
| E | Yellow & White | | | | |
| *3023 | Sporting Cat Cricketer | 4⅛ | | | |
| *3027 | Sporting Cat Bowls | 4⅛ | | | |
| *3039 | Sporting Cat Tennis | 4⅛ | | | |

*In this projected series, only the Footballer Cats were put into limited production.
†Flower decoration in three different colourways

# English Country Folk

(All models carry a Beswick backstamp)

These very collectable, gloss finish, humorous animal characters were introduced in September 1993, with further additions in mid 1994. Portraying animals dressed as humans, they herald a new collection, with close attention to detail. Each one carries its own 'ECF' number and these are listed below.

| Model No | Name of Model | ECF No | Height inches | Current Value £ | US$ | Production Period |
|---|---|---|---|---|---|---|
| 3417 | Gentleman Pig | 4 | 5¾ | 24·95 | RRP | 1993-C |
| 3418 | Huntsman Fox | 1 | 5¾ | 24·95 | RRP | 1993-C |
| 3419 | Fisherman Otter | 2 | 5¾ | 24·95 | RRP | 1993-C |
| 3420 | Gardener Rabbit | 3 | 6 | 24·95 | RRP | 1993-C |
| 3421 | Hiker Badger | 6 | 5¼ | 24·95 | RRP | 1993-C |
| 3422 | Shepherd Sheepdog | 5 | 6¾ | 24·95 | RRP | 1993-C |
| 3447 | Mrs Rabbit Baking | 7 | 5½ | 24·95 | RRP | 1994-C |
| 3448 | Lady Pig | 8 | 5½ | 24·95 | RRP | 1994-C |

# Pig Prom Musicians

(Special 'Beswick Ware' backstamp for 1994 only)

This superb set of gloss finish humorous pig musicians, each playing a different musical instrument, was introduced in 1994. For this introductory year only, the early 'Beswick Ware' backstamp was used on the first six models, thereafter, the plain 'Beswick England' backstamp was applied. The next three models also had this plain backstamp, as do the final three pieces which were specially commissioned by John Sinclair of Sheffield, in editions of 2000 each. These final three are colourways of earlier models and not different to them in any other way.

Each of the first nine models is a different breed and all have a separate 'PP' number which is listed below.

The unusually short run of this series will probably make them quite collectable and I think that the 'Beswick Ware' series (1-6) and number 9 will become much sought after with numbers 10 to 12 being collected by the real enthusiast.

| Model No | Name of Model | PP No | Height inches | Current Value £ | US$ | Production Period |
|---|---|---|---|---|---|---|
| 3440 | Andrew — Cymbal Player (blue waistcoat) Gloucester Old Spot | 4 | 4¾ | 30-35 | 60-70 | 1994-1996 |
| 3443 | Mathew— Trumpet Player Large White | 2 | 6 | 30-35 | 60-70 | 1994-1996 |
| 3444 | David — Flute Player Tamworth | 3 | 5¼ | 30-35 | 60-70 | 1994-1996 |
| 3446 | John — Conductor Vietnamese Pot-Bellied | 1 | 4⅝ | 30-35 | 60-70 | 1994-1996 |
| 3453 | Daniel — Violin Player Saddleback | 5 | 5¼ | 30-35 | 60-70 | 1994-1996 |
| 3454 | Michael — Bass Drum Player Large Black | 6 | 4¾ | 30-35 | 60-70 | 1994-1996 |

| Model No | Name of Model | PP No | Height inches | Current Value £ | US$ | Production Period |
|---|---|---|---|---|---|---|
| 3532 | James— Triangle Player Tamworth Piglet | 7 | 4 | 30-35 | 60-70 | 1995-1996 |
| 3564 | Richard — French Horn Player (red waistcoat) German Pietrain | 8 | 5½ | 35-40 | 70-80 | 1996 only |
| 3562 | Christopher — Guitar Player (yellow waistcoat) – Berkshire | 9 | 4¾ | 35-40 | 70-80 | 1996 only |
| 3440 | George — Cymbal Player (green waistcoat) Gloucester Old Spot | 10 | 4¾ | 35-40 | 70-80 | 1996 only |
| 3562 | Thomas— Guitar Player (green waistcoat) – Berkshire | 11 | 4¾ | 32 | 64 | 1997 only |
| 3564 | Benjamin — French Horn Player (blue waistcoat) German Pietrain | 12 | 4¾ | 32 | 64 | 1997 only |

# Figures

(All models carry a Beswick backstamp)

Beswick have produced a wide variety of figures. From 1894 they made the traditional Staffordshire types and continued production of these long after other manufacturers had ceased.

The first figure recorded in the existing pattern books was a smiling policeman directing traffic (303). This is an isolated model as the majority of the figures in the 1930s and 40s portrayed children, mostly modelled by Miss Greaves. Some were given names and these have been listed, where known, although it is not thought that the models were marked with the names.

During World War Two Beswick introduced their Kindergarten series, 'near' copies of the popular Hummel style figures made in Germany by Goebbels. Beswick exported most of these to America and Canada but, after the war, when Germany was again able to export, Beswick ceased production. As they were produced only throughout the war years, these pieces are now very rare. The original Hummel model number for each figure is recorded in the lists.

This cute style of figure was revived briefly in 1969 when Albert Hallam modelled a series of doll-like children based upon drawings in a book by Joan Welsh Anglund, entitled, A Friend Is Someone Who Loves You, first published in 1959.

In the opinion of many collectors the finest Beswick figures are those designed by Miss Granoska between 1951 and 1954. Most portray characters in national costume, often accompanied by animals. One set depicts obstinate donkeys and goats carrying panniers of apples and grapes, being led, pushed or ridden by European peasants, whilst another group features national dancers of the world.

During the 1950s a number of figures appeared on horse-back, ranging from Colin Melbourne's stylised clowns riding bare-back to more realistic portraits of huntsmen and soldiers in the saddle. The latter are classed under the horses group.

Beswick have also produced many figures inspired by characters from film and literature and these are listed in their appropriate section.

| Model No | Name of Model | Height inches | Current Value £ | US$ | Production Period |
|---|---|---|---|---|---|
| 303 | Policeman standing on box, with hand raised | — | 250-300 | 500-600 | 1935-1954 |
| 374 | Girl tasting honey (Felicity) | 5 | 250-300 | 500-600 | 1936-1954 |
| 375 | Girl in swimming costume (Bo-Bo) | 6 | 250-300 | 500-600 | 1936-1954 |
| 388 | Girl – finger in mouth (Tinker) | 5¾ | 250-300 | 500-600 | 1936-1954 |
| 389 | Girl sitting on rock with legs outstretched (Mermaid) | — | 250-300 | 500-600 | 1936-1954 |
| | | | 250-300 | 500-600 | 1936-1954 |
| 390 | Girl in breeze | 5½ | | | |
| 391 | Girl with hands in muff – on base (Prudence) | 7¼ | 250-300 | 500-600 | 1936-1954 |
| 437 | Girl with flared dress holding shoe (Pansie) | 4¾ | 250-300 | 500-600 | 1936-1954 |
| 438 | Girl with frilled dress arms stretched up (Pansie) | — | 250-300 | 500-600 | 1936-1954 |
| 441 | Lady, standing, with arms out and holding dress up on base (Nymph) | — | 250-300 | 500-600 | 1936-1954 |
| 442 | Lady, standing, with hands on hips – on base (Annabel) | 8 | 250-300 | 500-600 | 1936-1954 |
| 443 | Child, sitting | — | 250-300 | 500-600 | 1936-1954 |
| 501 | Clown | — | 250-300 | 500-600 | 1937-1954 |
| 622 | Mr Chamberlain | — | 250-300 | 500-600 | 1938-1940 |
| 751/1 | Boy Soldier facing left in front of sentry box (bookend) | 6 | 150-200 | 300-400 | 1939-1954 |
| 751/2 | Boy Soldier facing right in front of sentry box (bookend) | 6 | 150-200 | 300-400 | 1939-1954 |
| 903 | Bugle Boy (Hummel 97) | 6 | 200-250 | 400-500 | 1940-1948 |
| 904 | Book Worm (Hummel 3) | 5 | 200-250 | 400-500 | 1940-1948 |
| 905 | Goose Girl (Hummel 47) | 6¼ | 200-250 | 400-500 | 1940-1948 |
| 906 | Strolling Along (Hummel 5) | 4¾ | 200-250 | 400-500 | 1941-1948 |
| 908 | Stormy Weather (Hummel 71) | 6 | 200-250 | 400-500 | 1941-1948 |
| 909 | Puppy Love (Hummel 1) | 5¼ | 200-250 | 400-500 | 1941-1948 |
| 910 | Meditation (Hummel 13) | 5 | 200-250 | 400-500 | 1941-1948 |
| 911 | Max & Moritz (Hummel 123) | 5¾ | 200-250 | 400-500 | 1941-1948 |
| 912 | Farm Boy (Hummel 66) | 6 | 200-250 | 400-500 | 1941-1948 |
| 913 | Globe Trotter (Hummel 109) | 5 | 200-250 | 400-500 | 1941-1948 |
| 914 | Shepherd Boy (Hummel 64) | 4¼ | 200-250 | 400-500 | 1941-1948 |
| 924 | Winston Churchill, waving hat | 6 | 300-500 | 600-1000 | 1941-1954 |
| 940/1 | ARP Warden outside air raid shelter (book-end) | 6½ | 50-75 | 100-150 | 1941-1946 |
| 940/2 | Boy, girl and mother looking out of shelter (book-end) | 6 | 50-75 | 100-150 | 1941-1946 |
| 952/1 | Army Co-operation. Couple embracing, behind sandbag wall (book-end) | 5 | 50-75 | 100-150 | 1941-1946 |
| 952/2 | Soldier pulling pin from hand grenade behind sandbag wall (book-end) | 7 | 50-75 | 100-150 | 1941-1946 |
| †990 | Boy strumming banjo | 3 | 600-800 | 1200-1600 | 1942 only |
| 1010 | Fairy Crying | 6 | 300-500 | 600-1000 | 1944-1954 |
| 1011 | Fairy Drinking | 4 | 300-500 | 600-1000 | 1944-1954 |
| 1012 | Fairy Sewing | 4¾ | 300-500 | 600-1000 | 1944-1954 |
| 1013 | Fairy Baking | 6¼ | 300-500 | 600-1000 | 1944-1954 |
| 1020 | Madonna | 14 | 300-400 | 600-800 | 1945-1954 |
| 1086 | Clown & Dog on base | 7¼ | 200-300 | 400-600 | 1947-1958 |

| Model No | Name of Model | Height inches | Current Value £ | US$ | Production Period |
|---|---|---|---|---|---|
| 1087 | Jester sitting | 5 | 200-300 | 400-600 | 1947-1958 |
| 1091 | Gypsy Girl | $7\frac{1}{4}$ | 200-300 | 400-600 | 1947-1958 |
| 1093 | Hiker Boy | 6 | 200-300 | 400-600 | 1947-1954 |
| 1094 | Hiker Girl | 6 | 200-300 | 400-600 | 1947-1954 |
| 1096 | Sportsman & Dog | $6\frac{3}{4}$ | 200-300 | 400-600 | 1947-1958 |
| 1097 | Fruit Seller (Pedlar) | — | 200-300 | 400-600 | 1947-1958 |
| 1122 | Butcher Boy with basket | $5\frac{3}{4}$ | 200-300 | 400-600 | 1948-1958 |
| 1123 | Man with flower pot | $6\frac{1}{4}$ | 200-300 | 400-600 | 1948-1954 |
| 1124 | Shepherd Boy with two sheep under arm | $6\frac{1}{4}$ | 200-300 | 400-600 | 1948-1959 |
| 1125 | Scotsman in kilt | $6\frac{1}{4}$ | 200-300 | 400-600 | 1948-1954 |
| 1221 | Hungarian Girl with turkey | $7\frac{1}{4}$ | 150-200 | 300-400 | 1951-1962 |
| 1222 | Polish Girl with hen | 7 | 150-200 | 300-400 | 1951-1962 |
| 1223 | Spaniard pulling donkey with panniers of apples | $4\frac{1}{2}$ | 150-200 | 300-400 | 1951-1962 |
| 1224 | Spaniard pushing donkey with panniers of grapes | $4\frac{1}{2}$ | 150-200 | 300-400 | 1951-1962 |
| 1227 | Swedish Girl holding cockerel | 7 | 150-200 | 300-400 | 1952-1962 |
| 1230 | Danish Girl leading pig | $5\frac{3}{4}$ | 150-200 | 300-400 | 1952-1962 |
| 1234 | Italian Girl leading goat | $5\frac{1}{2}$ | 150-200 | 300-400 | 1952-1962 |
| 1238 | Italian Girl with goat eating hat | 6 | 150-200 | 300-400 | 1952-1962 |
| 1244 | Spanish Girl on donkey | $5\frac{1}{2}$ | 150-200 | 300-400 | 1952-1962 |
| 1245 | Spanish children on donkey | $4\frac{1}{2}$ | 150-200 | 300-400 | 1952-1962 |
| 1247 | Finnish Girl with duck | 7 | 150-200 | 300-400 | 1952-1962 |
| 1262 | Balinese Girl | $3\frac{1}{2}$ | 200-250 | 400-500 | 1952-1962 |
| 1263 | Indian Girl | $3\frac{1}{2}$ | 200-250 | 400-500 | 1952-1962 |
| 1320 | Siamese Dancer | $3\frac{1}{2}$ | 200-250 | 400-500 | 1953-1962 |
| 1321 | Japanese Dancer | $3\frac{1}{2}$ | 200-250 | 400-500 | 1953-1962 |
| 1333 | Chinese Dancer | $3\frac{1}{2}$ | 200-250 | 400-500 | 1954-1962 |
| 1334 | Hawaiian Dancer | $3\frac{1}{2}$ | 200-250 | 400-500 | 1954-1962 |
| 1347 | Susie Jamaica | 7 | 150-200 | 300-400 | 1954-1975 |
| 1470 | Clown on Horse (small) (CM series) | $5\frac{3}{4}$ | 200-250 | 400-500 | 1957-1963 |
| 1476 | Clown on horse (large) (CM series) | $8\frac{1}{2}$ | 250-300 | 500-600 | 1957-1963 |
| 1626 | Toy drummer ⎤ coloured | $2\frac{3}{8}$ | 50-60 | 100-120 | 1959-1966 |
| 1627 | Toy buglers ⎬ red and | $2\frac{3}{8}$ | 50-60 | 100-120 | 1959-1966 |
| 1628 | Toy guards ⎦ blue | $2\frac{3}{8}$ | 50-60 | 100-120 | 1959-1966 |
| 1737 | Man & Woman, sitting | $8\frac{3}{8}$ | 150-200 | 300-400 | 1961-1963 |
| 1766 | Road Gang: Foreman | — | 80-100 | 160-200 | 1961-1963 |
| 1767 | Road Gang: Digger | — | 80-100 | 160-200 | 1961-1963 |
| 1768 | Road Gang: Driller | — | 80-100 | 160-200 | 1961-1963 |
| 1769 | Road Gang: At Ease | — | 80-100 | 160-200 | 1961-1963 |
| 1801/2 | Pianist & Piano (See also 1803 in Cats Section) | 3 | 75-100 each | 150-200 | 1963-1969 |
| 1804 | Boy without spectacles | $3\frac{5}{8}$ | 100-150 | 200-300 | 1963-1969 |
| 1805 | Boy with spectacles (See also 1824 in Dogs Section) | 3 | 100-150 | 200-300 | 1963-1969 |
| 1825 | Boy with guitar | 3 | 100-150 | 200-300 | 1963-1969 |
| 1826 | Girl with harp | $3\frac{5}{8}$ | 100-150 | 200-300 | 1963-1969 |
| 1878 | Welsh Lady | 5 | 50-60 | 100-125 | 1963-1969 |
| 1937 | Bust of Lady (C.M.C. on base) | 6 | 50-60 | 100-125 | 1964-1965 |
| 1993 | Lady with fan | $7\frac{1}{2}$ | 200-300 | 400-600 | 1964-1965 |
| 1994 | Lady with hat | $7\frac{1}{2}$ | 200-300 | 400-600 | 1964-1965 |
| 1995 | Lady in ball gown | 7 | 200-300 | 400-600 | 1964-1965 |
| 2181 | Knight of St John | $6\frac{3}{4}$ | 250-300 | 500-600 | 1968-1969 |

| Model No | Name of Model | Height inches | Current Value £ | US$ | Production Period |
|---|---|---|---|---|---|
| 2272 | Anglund Boy | 4⅜ | 100-125 | 200-250 | 1970-1971 |
| 2293 | Anglund Girl with doll behind back | 4⅜ | 100-125 | 200-250 | 1970-1971 |
| 2317 | Anglund Girl with flowers | 4¾ | 100-125 | 200-250 | 1971 only |

†Not put into production

# Little Loveables

This colourful series of ten different clowns were modelled by Amanda Hughes-Lubeck (8) and Warren Platt (2) in the John Beswick Studio, at Longton, under the watchful eye of Graham Tongue.

They first appeared at the end of 1992 and were notable in having suitable names printed on top of the base. Very shortly after their introduction, the name on model nos LL3, 10 and 17 — 'God Loves Me' was changed to 'Please' and this has naturally meant that the short supply of 'God Loves Me' has put a premium on this particular one.

The other interesting fact is that LL15-LL21 were Parian versions for the American market. Each model is available in two different colour combinations (with a gloss finish) and a third Parian version which has a matt finish. There is also a set without any names on the base.

Full details of the separate LL numbers together with the Beswick model numbers are given in the list which follows:

| LL No | Model No | Model Name | Gloss or Matt | Colour of Stripes | Colour of Spots | Size | Current Value £ | US$ | Production Period |
|---|---|---|---|---|---|---|---|---|---|
| 1 | 3328 | Happy Birthday | G | Pale Pink | Bright Orange | 4½ | 20-25 | 40-50 | 1992-1994 |
| 2 | 3320 | I Love You | G | Light Green | Pale Pink | 4½ | 20-25 | 40-50 | 1992-1994 |
| *3 | 3336 | God Loves Me | G | Light Green | Turquoise | 3¾ | 50-75 | 100-150 | 1992-1993 |
| 4 | 3361 | Just For You | G | Pale Pink | Turquoise | 4½ | 20-25 | 40-50 | 1992-1994 |
| 5 | 3331 | To Mother | G | Turquoise | Purple | 4½ | 20-25 | 40-50 | 1992-1994 |
| 6 | 3340 | Congratulations | G | Dark Green | Pale Pink | 4½ | 20-25 | 40-50 | 1992-1994 |
| 7 | 3334 | Passed | G | Lilac | Pale Pink | 3 | 20-25 | 40-50 | 1992-1994 |
| 8 | 3328 | Happy Birthday | G | Orange/Yellow | Dark Green | 4½ | 20-25 | 40-50 | 1992-1994 |
| 9 | 3320 | I Love You | G | Lilac | Orange/Yellow | 4½ | 20-25 | 40-50 | 1992-1994 |
| *10 | 3336 | God Loves Me | G | Orange/Yellow | Powder Blue | 3¾ | 50-75 | 100-150 | 1992-1993 |
| 11 | 3361 | Just For You | G | Orange/Yellow | Mint Green | 4½ | 20-25 | 40-50 | 1992-1994 |
| 12 | 3331 | To Mother | G | Peach/Yellow | Pale Pink | 4½ | 20-25 | 40-50 | 1992-1994 |
| 13 | 3340 | Congratulations | G | Turquoise | Orange/Yellow | 4½ | 20-25 | 40-50 | 1992-1994 |
| 14 | 3334 | Passed | G | Pale Blue | Bright Orange | 3 | 20-25 | 40-50 | 1992-1994 |
| 15 | 3407 | Happy Birthday | M | Coral | Leaf Green | 4½ | 75-100 | 150-200 | 1992-1993 |
| 16 | 3406 | I Love You | M | Dover Green | Pale Yellow | 4½ | 75-100 | 150-200 | 1992-1993 |
| **17 | 3410 | God Loves Me | M | Crimson | Pale Yellow | 3¾ | 100-125 | 200-250 | 1992-1993 |

| LL No | Model No | Model Name | Gloss or Matt | Colour of Stripes | Colour of Spots | Size | Current Value £ | US$ | Production Period |
|---|---|---|---|---|---|---|---|---|---|
| 18 | 3412 | Just For You | M | Bright Yellow | Bright Blue | 4½ | 75-100 | 150-200 | 1992-1993 |
| 19 | 3408 | To Mother | M | Leaf Green | Orange | 4½ | 75-100 | 150-200 | 1992-1993 |
| 20 | 3411 | Congratulations | M | Bright Blue | Bright Red | 4½ | 75-100 | 150-200 | 1992-1993 |
| 21 | 3409 | Passed | M | Bright Blue | Orange | 3 | 75-100 | 150-200 | 1992-1993 |
| 22 | 3328 | No Name *Sandy coloured base* | G | Pale Pink | Bright Orange | 4½ | 75-100 | 150-200 | 1993 only |
| 23 | 3320 | No Name *Sandy coloured base* | G | Light Green | Pale Pink | 4½ | 75-100 | 150-200 | 1993 only |
| 24 | 3336 | No Name *Sandy coloured base* | G | Light Green | Turquoise | 3¾ | 75-100 | 150-200 | 1993 only |
| 25 | 3361 | No Name *Sandy coloured base* | G | Pale Pink | Turquoise Blue | 4½ | 75-100 | 150-200 | 1993 only |
| 26 | 3331 | No Name *Sandy coloured base* | G | Turquoise | Purple | 4¼ | 75-100 | 150-200 | 1993 only |
| 27 | 3340 | No Name *Sandy coloured base* | G | Dark Green | Pale Pink | 4½ | 75-100 | 150-200 | 1993 only |
| 28 | 3334 | No Name *Sandy coloured base* | G | Lilac | Pale Pink | 3 | 75-100 | 150-200 | 1993 only |
| 29 | 3331 | To Daddy | G | Turquoise | Mint Green | 4½ | 30-35 | 60-70 | 1994 only |
| 30 | 3389 | Merry Christmas | G | Bright Red | Dark Green & toys | 4 | 30-35 | 60-70 | 1993-1994 |
| 31 | 3388 | Good Luck | G | Pale Pink | Mint Green | 4¼ | 30-35 | 60-70 | 1993-1994 |
| 32 | 3390 | Get Well Soon | G | Dark Green | Vivid Purple | 4¼ | 30-35 | 60-70 | 1994 only |
| 33 | 3336 | Please | G | Light Green | Turquoise | 3¾ | 30-35 | 60-70 | 1993-1994 |
| 34 | 3336 | Please | G | Orange/Yellow | Powder Blue | 3¾ | 30-35 | 60-70 | 1993-1994 |
| 35 | 3410 | Please | M | Crimson | Pale Yellow | 3¾ | 200-250 | 400-500 | 1995 only |
| †36 | 3320 | I Love Beswick | G | 'Beswick' Green | Yellow | 4½ | 100-125 | 200-250 | 1995 only |

*Name changed to 'Please' and transferred to LL33 and LL34
**Name changed to 'Please' 4/93 and transferred to LL35.
†Beswick Collectors Circle special model

# Little Likeables

(All models carry a John Beswick backstamp)

This collection of bone china animal sculptures from the John Beswick Studio of Royal Doulton, broke new ground when they were first announced in the January 1985 price list. All white, with a minimum of gold and pastel colouring and with a gloss finish, they immediately set new standards for the Beswick animal studies and had an irresistable charm of their own.

They were never illustrated in any form of catalogue, other than trade issues and so very little is known about them.

The series is very collectable and extremely well modelled by Robert Tabbenor and Diane Griffiths and should be on the 'shopping list' of every dedicated Beswick collector.

By the end of 1986 they were beginning to be difficult to find and when the January 1987 price list was issued, the reason became clear, they had been withdrawn!

Each model was individually priced in an attractive gift box and prices ranged betweed £10 and £15. The following collectors list gives all the information known about each model.

| Model No | Name of Model | Height inches | Modeller | Current Value £ | US$ |
|---|---|---|---|---|---|
| LL1 | 'Family gathering' (Hen and 2 chicks) | 4½ | Diane Griffiths | 25-30 | 50-60 |
| LL2 | 'Watching The World Go By' (Frog) | 3¾ | Robert Tabbenor | 35-40 | 70-80 |
| LL3 | 'Hide and Sleep' (Pig and 2 piglets) | 3¼ | Robert Tabbenor | 30-35 | 60-70 |
| LL4 | 'My Pony' (Pony) | 7¼ | Diane Griffiths | 30-35 | 60-70 |
| LL5 | 'On Top Of The World' (Elephant) | 3¾ | Diane Grffiths | 30-35 | 60-70 |
| LL6 | 'Treat Me Gently' (Fawn) | 4½ | Diane Griffiths | 30-35 | 60-70 |
| LL7 | 'Out At Last' (Duckling) | 3¼ | Robert Tabbenor | 25-30 | 50-60 |
| LL8 | 'Cats Chorus' | 4¾ | Robert Tabbenor | 30-35 | 60-70 |

# Thunderbirds

(All carry a special Beswick backstamp)

To celebrate the 30th anniversary of this popular TV childrens programme, Lawleys By Post commissioned the John Beswick Studio of Royal Doulton to create a collection of six 4" high busts of the most popular characters from the series. Modelled by William K Harper in 1992 as a numbered edition of 2500 they were only available, by post, in a set of six, at a price of £237.

It is believed that, only about 750 sets were actually produced and sold as a numbered set. This would make the series very collectable in the future.

| Model No | Name of Model | Height inches | Current value £ | US$ | Production Period |
|---|---|---|---|---|---|
| 3337 | Lady Penelope | 4 | 65-75 | 130-150 | 1992-1993 |
| 3339 | Brains | 4 | 65-75 | 130-150 | 1992-1993 |
| 3344 | Scott Tracy | 4 | 65-75 | 130-150 | 1992-1993 |
| 3345 | Virgil Tracy | 4 | 65-75 | 130-150 | 1992-1993 |
| 3346 | Parker | 4 | 65-75 | 130-150 | 1992-1993 |
| 3348 | The Hood | 4 | 65-75 | 130-150 | 1992-1993 |

# Studio Sculptures (Resin)

This range of animal and bird studies was created by Design Manager Harry Sales and introduced in January 1985.

A new bonded ceramic body was used, which has the ability of capturing all the minute detail of each subject and literally brings it to life in a three-dimensional re-creation of the original drawing.

The initial sculpture entails a great deal of intricate modelling to achieve this and it is the final hand decoration on the finished product which really brings each sculpture to life.

Each item was separately boxed in specially designed packaging and some were available on polished hardwood bases.

The shortest production runs were of model numbers 26 to 30 (inclusive) which were only available for six months.

A green baize is applied to the whole of the base on each model and an adhesive label is then applied on top of this, giving model details.

It should be noted that model numbers 23 to 25 (inclusive) were not produced.

| Model No | Name of Model | Size inches | Current Value £ | US$ | Production Period |
|---|---|---|---|---|---|
| **BEATRIX POTTER SERIES** | | | | | |
| SS1 | Timmy Willie | 4¼ | 40-50 | 80-100 | 1985 only |
| *SS2 | Flopsy Bunnies | 5 | 75-100 | 150-200 | 1985 only |
| *SS3 | Mr Jeremy Fisher | 4 | 75-100 | 150-200 | 1985 only |
| *SS4 | Peter Rabbit | 7 | 75-100 | 150-200 | 1985 only |
| *SS11 | Mrs Tiggy Winkle | 5 | 75-100 | 150-200 | 1985 only |
| SS26 | Yock Yock (in the tub) | 1⅞ | 150-175 | 300-350 | 1/86-6/86 |
| SS27 | Peter Rabbit (in the watering can) | 3¼ | 150-175 | 300-350 | 1/86-6/86 |
| | | | | | |
| **YOUNG FRIENDS SERIES** | | | | | |
| SS5 | 'Puppy Love' (one dog washing another) black & brown, also black & white | 4½ | 40-50 | 80-100 | 1985 only |
| SS6 | 'I Spy' (two kittens in basket) available intabby or white | 4½ | 40-50 | 80-100 | 1985 only |
| SS16 | 'Menu For Today' (puppy and kitten with cat food) brown & white or brown & tabby | 3½ | 40-50 | 80-100 | 1985 only |
| SS17 | 'Sharing' (dog & cat with bowl of milk) | 3½ | 40-50 | 80-100 | 1985 only |
| | | | | | |
| **COUNTRYSIDE SERIES** | | | | | |
| SS8 | 'Contentment' (brown & white rabbit & young) also available in black & white | 4¾ | 40-50 | 80-100 | 1985 only |
| SS9 | 'Bright Eyes' (brown rabbit) also in black | 4½ | 40-50 | 80-100 | 1985 only |
| SS10 | 'Mind How You Go' (goose & goslings) | 5¼ | 50-60 | 100-120 | 1985 only |
| *SS13 | 'Happy Landing' (swan) | 5 | 50-60 | 100-120 | 1985 only |
| SS14 | 'The Chase' (3 dogs scrambling over a wall) | — | 50-60 | 100-120 | 1985 only |
| *SS15 | 'Hide and Seek' (3 dogsplaying in a rock pool) | 4½ | 50-60 | 100-120 | 1985 only |
| SS18 | 'Planning Ahead' (squirrel with nuts) | 3 | 30-40 | 60-80 | 1985 only |
| SS19 | 'Early Bird' (wren) | 2½ | 20-30 | 40-60 | 6/85-12/85 |
| SS20 | Golden Retriever | — | 40-50 | 80-100 | 1/85-12/85 |
| SS21 | Pointer | — | 40-50 | 80-100 | 6/85-12/85 |
| SS22 | English Setter | — | 40-50 | 80-100 | 6/85-12/85 |
| SS28 | Robin | 2¾ | 20-30 | 40-60 | 1/86-6/86 |
| SS29 | Blue Tit | 2¾ | 20-30 | 40-60 | 1/86-6/86 |
| SS30 | Chaffinch | 2¾ | 20-30 | 40-60 | 1/86-6/86 |
| *on wood base | | | | | |
| | | | | | |
| **THELWELL SERIES** | | | | | |
| SS7 | 'I forgive you' (in grey or bay) | 4 | 75-100 | 150-200 | 1985 only |
| SS12 | 'Early Bath' (in grey or bay) | 4¾ | 75-100 | 150-200 | 1985 only |

# Beswick Bears (Resin)

These superb resin models were produced under licence by the Royal Doulton Retail Division and marketed through Royal Doulton Shops, Lawleys and Factory Shops. Manufacturerd by Border Fine Arts, they were packed in the standard green John Beswick box, with 'Beswick Bears' printed on the side.

An additional gold sticker identified the particular model inside the box. The green baise base had a green adhesive label giving the model name and number together with a short rhyme.

The characters are all doing something different at a Teddy Bears picnic and the colours used on each model blend well and present a very natural group.

Available only during 1993 at very few outlets and at a very affordable price of £9.95, these models could easily become a very collectable series. Each model is impressed with the Beswick 'B' mark.

| Model No | Name of Model | Height inches | Current Value £ | US$ | Production Period |
|---|---|---|---|---|---|
| BB001 | William | 2¼ | 40-50 | 80-100 | 1993 only |
| BB002 | Billly | 4 | 40-50 | 80-100 | 1993 only |
| BB003 | Harry | 3¼ | 40-50 | 80-100 | 1993 only |
| BB004 | Bobby | 4 | 40-50 | 80-100 | 1993 only |
| BB005 | James | 3¼ | 40-50 | 80-100 | 1993 only |
| BB006 | Susie | 3½ | 40-50 | 80-100 | 1993 only |
| BB007 | Angela | 3¼ | 40-50 | 80-100 | 1993 only |
| BB008 | Charlotte | 4 | 40-50 | 80-100 | 1993 only |
| BB009 | Sam | 3½ | 40-50 | 80-100 | 1993 only |
| BB010 | Lizzy | 2¼ | 40-50 | 80-100 | 1993 only |
| BB011 | Emily | 3½ | 40-50 | 80-100 | 1993 only |
| BB012 | Sarah | 3¼ | 40-50 | 80-100 | 1993 only |

# Country Cousins (Resin)

Made of Resin, manufactured in (the country of) China and marketed by the Royal Doulton Retail Division, this series of 17 different small animals has a green baize base with a sticker describing the model and marked 'Beswick International'. Introduced in October 1994 and withdrawn 12 months later. Numbers PM2110, 2117 and 2118 where not used

| Model No | Name of Model | Current Value £ | US$ |
|---|---|---|---|
| PM 2101 | Sweet Suzie | 15-20 | 30-40 |
| PM 2102 | Peter | 15-20 | 30-40 |
| PM 2103 | Harry | 15-20 | 30-40 |
| PM 2104 | Michael | 15-20 | 30-40 |
| PM 2105 | Bertram | 15-20 | 30-40 |
| PM 2106 | Leonardo | 15-20 | 30-40 |
| PM 2107 | Lilly | 15-20 | 30-40 |
| PM 2108 | Patrick | 15-20 | 30-40 |
| PM 2109 | Jamie | 15-20 | 30-40 |
| PM 2111 | Mum and Lizzy | 20-25 | 40-50 |
| PM 2112 | Molly and Timmy | 20-25 | 40-50 |
| PM 2113 | Polly and Sarah | 20-25 | 40-50 |
| PM 2114 | Ted and Bill | 20-25 | 40-50 |
| PM 2115 | Jack and Daisy | 20-25 | 40-50 |
| PM 2116 | Alison and Debbie | 20-25 | 40-50 |
| PM 2119 | Robert and Rosie | 20-25 | 40-50 |
| PM 2120 | Sammy | 15-20 | 30-40 |

# Wall Plaques and Masks

(All models carry a Beswick backstamp)

Between the wars there was a rather bizarre fashion for adorning the living room walls with pottery portraits of chic young ladies or colourful characters. The Beswick artists catered for this trend between 1934 and 1939 and in that time produced no less than twenty different models. Varying in size between three and twelve inches, these wall masks were described as novelties in the catalogues and were available in assorted colourways, including a matt white glaze finish, at between two and three shillings each (10p and 15p). The fashionable ladies and cute little girls seem to have been the most popular and the modeller, Miss Greaves, has portrayed them with the very latest accessories, jaunty berets or cloche hats.

Appealing to a different taste were the character masks featuring either a Jester, an Indian, a Patriotic Soldier or the favourite Dickens characters Tony Weller and MrMicawber. On the reverse of Mr Micawber, the eternal optimist, is his famous line "until something turns up, I have nothing to bestow but advice". The Dickens subjects were the speciality of Mr Watkin who later modelled the same personalities in the form of character jugs.

*Lady wall mask 277.*

*Three of the wall plaques. Top left: Life's A Melody, 739; Top right: When you are up to your neck, 740;Bottom: The Gleaners 507.*

Human faces were not the only subjects considered suitable for wall plaques; Beswick also produced bas-relief galleons and yachts, baskets of flowers, butterflies and the famous flights of birds. So distinctive are they that they have been catalogued in a section of their own.

| Model No | Name of Model | Height inches | Current Value £ | US$ | Production Period |
|---|---|---|---|---|---|
| 197 | Girl with beret | 6 | 200-250 | 400-500 | 1934-1954 |
| 263 | Galleon | 10 | 75-100 | 150-200 | 1934-1954 |
| 274 | Tony Weller | 7½ | 75-100 | 150-200 | 1934-1954 |
| 277 | Lady with beret in profile | 4½ | 200-250 | 400-500 | 1934-1954 |
| 279 | Jester | 5¼ | 75-100 | 150-200 | 1934-1954 |
| 280 | Mr Micawber | 9 | 75-100 | 150-200 | 1934-1954 |
| 282 | Indian | 7½ | 75-100 | 150-200 | 1934-1954 |
| 314 | Girl with curly hair & beret | 9½ | 200-250 | 400-500 | 1934-1954 |
| 362 | Girl with beret & scarf | — | 200-250 | 400-500 | 1935-1954 |
| 363 | Lady with beret & scarf in profile | — | 200-250 | 400-500 | 1935-1954 |
| 364 | Girl with beret & pom-pom | — | 200-250 | 400-500 | 1935-1954 |
| 365 | Girl with beret | — | 200-250 | 400-500 | 1935-1954 |
| 366 | Girl with hat | — | 200-250 | 400-500 | 1935-1954 |
| 367 | Lady with hat & scarf in profile | — | 200-250 | 400-500 | 1935-1954 |
| 380 | Girl with hat | 9½ | 200-250 | 400-500 | 1936-1954 |
| 392 | Cherub lying down | 6¼ | 200-250 | 400-500 | 1936-1954 |
| 393 | Girl with plait | 8½ | 200-250 | 400-500 | 1936-1954 |
| 419 | Floral wall hoop | 12 | 100-150 | 200-300 | 1936-1954 |
| 420 | Floral wall triangle | — | 100-150 | 200-300 | 1936-1954 |
| 436 | Lady with beads | 12 | 200-300 | 400-600 | 1936-1954 |
| 449 | Lady with hat & spotted scarf | 12½ | 200-300 | 400-600 | 1936-1954 |
| 457 | Genie | 9¼ | 150-200 | 300-400 | 1936-1954 |
| 483 | Girl – hands behind head | 9 | 300-400 | 600-800 | 1937-1954 |
| 507 | The Gleaners | 11 | 150-200 | 300-400 | 1937-1940 |
| 508 | The Angelus | 11 | 150-200 | 300-400 | 1937-1940 |
| 551 | Basket of Flowers | 10 | 100-125 | 200-250 | 1937-1954 |
| 556 | Basket of Flowers | 10½ | 100-125 | 200-250 | 1937-1954 |
| 557 | Bowl of Flowers | 6½ | 100-125 | 200-250 | 1937-1954 |
| 564 | Bullrushes | 14 | 100-125 | 200-250 | 1937-1940 |
| 565 | Bowl of Flowers | 5½ | 100-125 | 200-250 | 1937-1954 |
| 571 | Bowl of Roses | 5¼ | 100-125 | 200-250 | 1937-1954 |
| 612 | Boy with red hair | 7¼ | 250-300 | 500-600 | 1938-1954 |
| 614 | Butterfly | — | 80-100 | 160-200 | 1938-1954 |
| 710 | Lovers | 8 | 150-200 | 300-400 | 1939-1940 |
| 714 | Three Cherubs 'Hear no evil' Etc | 6 x 4½ | 200-250 | 400-500 | 1939-1940 |
| 715 | 'A world without friends would be like a garden without flowers' | 9½ x 7½ | 200-250 | 400-500 | 1939-1940 |
| 719 | 'One of the best things to have up your sleeve is a funny bone' | 9½ x 7½ | 200-250 | 400-500 | 1939-1940 |
| 723 | 'Those who bring sunshine to the lives of others cannot keep it from themselves' | 9½ x 7½ | 200-250 | 400-500 | 1939-1940 |
| 724 | 'Don't worry it may never happen' | 8 x 8¾ | 200-250 | 400-500 | 1939-1940 |
| 739 | 'Life's a melody if you'll only hum the tune' | 8 x 8¾ | 200-250 | 400-500 | 1939-1940 |

| Model No | Name of Model | Height inches | Current Value £ | US$ | Production Period |
|---|---|---|---|---|---|
| 740 | 'When you are up to your neck in hot water think of the kettle and sing' | 8 x 8¾ | 200-250 | 400-500 | 1939-1940 |
| 741 | Lovers | 8 | 150-200 | 300-400 | 1939-1945 |
| 837 | Plain Plaque | 16 dia | 75-100 | 150-200 | 1940-1954 |
| 842 | Gargoyle Mask | 4½ x 5½ | 100-150 | 200-300 | 1940-1954 |
| 1632 | Yacht No. 2242 | 7¾ | 100-150 | 200-300 | 1959-1962 |
| *2233 | Cat and Dog | 9 x 6¼ | 75-100 | 150-200 | 1969-1970 |
| *2235 | Basset Hound | 9 x 6¼ | 75-100 | 150-200 | 1969-1970 |
| *2236 | Cat | 9 x 6¼ | 75-100 | 150-200 | 1969-1970 |
| *2268 | Poodle | 6 x 4¾ | 75-100 | 150-200 | 1969-1970 |

*Concave models in white matt finish

# Special Commissions

Specially commissioned models carrying the Beswick backstamp

## Beswick Collectors Circle/Club

| Model No | Name of Model | Size inches | Current Value £ | US$ | Year of issue | Number supplied |
|---|---|---|---|---|---|---|
| 818 | Black standing shire horse | 8½ | 500-550 | 1000-1100 | 1990 | 135 |
| 1439 | 'Red' Friesian Bull | 4¾ | 300-350 | 600-700 | 1992 | 129 |
| 1362 | 'Red' Friesian Cow | 4½ | 300-350 | 600-700 | 1992 | 130 |
| 2690 | 'Red' Friesian Calf (lying) | 2¼ | 150-200 | 300-400 | 1992 | 132 |
| 3062 | 'Chocolate' labrador dog (matt) | 5¼ | 40-50 | 80-100 | 1993 | 93 |
| 3320 | 'Little Loveable' Clown LL36 "I Love Beswick" | 4½ | 100-125 | 200-250 | 1995 | 442 |
| — | Shetland Pony DA185 Skewbald 'Hollydell Dixie' | 5¼ | 100-150 | 200-300 | 1995 | 553 |
| 975 | Black trotting shire horse | 8¾ | 100-200 | 200-400 | 1996 | 735 |

Initial issue of all these models was only to members of the Beswick Collectors Circle/Club.

There are two more models which are going to be available to members of the Beswick Collectors Club as follows:

| Name of Model | Colourway | Shape no | Year of issue | £ | $ |
|---|---|---|---|---|---|
| Mare | Dun gloss | 976 | 1997 only | 50 | 100 |
| Foal | Dun gloss | 947 | 1997 only | 25 | 50 |

## Peter Rabbit and Friends

A special edition of one of the current Beatrix Potter models with a Gold Beswick backstamp has been commissioned by 'Peter Rabbit and Friends'. His two coat buttons are also gold. The model is shape number 3242 and is entitled 'Peter Rabbit and the Red Pocket Handkerchief'. Price £29.95/$60

## UK International Ceramics

| Model No | Name of Model | Size inches | Current Value £ | US$ | Year of issue | Number supplied |
|---|---|---|---|---|---|---|
| 3547 | Droopy | 4¼ | 40 | 80 | 1996 | 2000 |
| 3549 | Jerry | 3 | 40 | 80 | 1995 | 2000 |
| 3552 | Tom | 4¼ | 40 | 80 | 1995 | 2000 |
| *3568 | Sitting Meerkat | 3 | 45 | 90 | 1996 | 1250 |
| *3571 | Standing Meerkat | 3½ | 45 | 90 | 1996 | 1250 |

| Model No | Name of Model | Size inches | Current Value £ | US$ | Year of issue | Number supplied |
|---|---|---|---|---|---|---|
| 3577 | Pebbles | 3½ | | | 1997 | 2000 |
| 3579 | Betty Rubble | 4 | 40 | 80 | 1996 | 2000 |
| 3583 | Wilma Flintstone | 4¾ | 40 | 80 | 1996 | 2000 |
| 3584 | Barney Rubble | 3¾ | 40 | 80 | 1996 | 2000 |
| 3587 | Bam-Bam | 3½ | | | 1997 | 2000 |
| 3588 | Fred Flintstone | 4¾ | 40 | 80 | 1996 | 2000 |
| 3590 | Dino | 5 | | | 1997 | 2000 |

*only available at the Dunstable UK Doulton Fair, October 1996

# Doulton Fairs in the UK

## John Sinclair, Sheffield

| Model No | Name of Model | Size inches | Current Value £ | US$ | Year of issue | Number supplied |
|---|---|---|---|---|---|---|
| 3581 | Top Cat | 4½ | 45 | 90 | 1996 | 2000 |
| 3586 | Choo-Choo | 4½ | 45 | 90 | 1996 | 2000 |
| 3624 | Fancy Fancy | 4½ | 40 | 80 | 1997 | 2000 |
| 3627 | Benny | 4 | 40 | 80 | 1997 | 2000 |
| 3671* | Office Dibble | | | | 1998 | 2000 |
| 3673* | Spook | | | | 1998 | 2000 |
| 3674* | Brain | | | | 1998 | 2000 |

*Prototype models only, at this stage

## John Sinclair, Sheffield

| Model No | Name of Model | Size inches | Current Value £ | US$ | Year of issue | Number supplied |
|---|---|---|---|---|---|---|
| 3440/PP10 | George (Pig Prom) Cymbal Player (Dark green waistcoat) | 4¾ | 35-40 | 70-80 | 1996 | 2000 |
| 3562/PP11 | Thomas (Pig Prom) Guitar Player (Light green waistcoat) | 4¾ | 32 | 65 | 1997 | 2000 |
| 3564/PP12 | Benjamin (Pig Prom) French Horn Player (Blue waistcoat) | 4¾ | 32 | 65 | 1997 | 2000 |

## Doug Middlewick, Widecombe-in-the-Moor

| Model No | Name of Model | Size inches | Current Value £ | US$ | Year of issue | Number supplied |
|---|---|---|---|---|---|---|
| 1642/2 | Dartmoor Pony Champion 'Warlord' | 6¼ | 45 | 90 | 1996 | 1500 |
| * | Dartmoor Pony Mare Champion 'Another Bunch' | 6 | 60 | 120 | 1997 | 1500 |
| * | Dartmoor Pony Foal lying | | | | 1998 | 1500 |

*New model

## Believed to be for a North American bank

| Model No | Name of Model | Size inches | Current Value £ | US$ | Year of issue | Number supplied |
|---|---|---|---|---|---|---|
| 3021 | Cream Unicorn on china base | 9¼ | 150-200 | 300-400 | 1987 | 100 app |

# Part Three: Decorative Wares

(All models carry a Beswick backstamp, except 1988 re-introductions for Whyte & Mackay. Since 1988 they are marked Royal Doulton)

## Advertising Ware

China and earthenware are ideal advertising media. They are durable, easy to clean and before the advent of plastic, they dominated the shop shelves.

Even today, although they are usually more expensive to produce than plastic they are still the chosen promotional tools for many breweries and distillers, who argue that a finely modelled ceramic decanter is less likely to be thrown away than a plain glass bottle and so their advertisement is more enduring. For over twenty years Beswick were responsible for the figurative whisky containers, many in the form of animals, for Peter Thomson of Perth and some of these are still being made today, but now with the Whyte & Mackay stamp. Beswick revived their association with Bass by re-issuing the Lord Mayor jug (first produced in 1961) for a short period in 1987.

Double Diamond was the first beer to be promoted by Beswick and the brewer's well-known city gent character was modelled as a teapot in 1958, followed by a jug and a wall-plaque in 1960. Other familiar pub artifacts of this period include the Babycham fawn and the Courage cockerel, although few of these were made. However, Beswick did not only cater for the spirit trade, their first recorded advertising piece was for Heatmaster who made teapots encased in thermal jackets. For this firm they made a liqueur set with the decanter in the form of a friar. It is not known what connection was intended between the liqueur container and Heatmaster's products, other than that they are all warming!

One of the most unusual advertising pieces in the collection features a little cobbler stitching a shoe which was made to celebrate Timpson's centenary in 1965.

| Model No | Name of Model | Height inches | Current Value £ | US$ | Production Period |
|---|---|---|---|---|---|
| 1201 | Friar Liqueur Set comprising tray & six measures for Heatmaster | 8¼ | 60-80 | 120-175 | 1950-1954 |
| 1517 | Double Diamond man container | 8 | 100-150 | 200-300 | 1958-1965 |
| 1544 | Barrel Lamp with tap | — | 30-40 | 60-80 | 1958-1965 |
| 1587 | Small Barrel (Sherry) | 4¼ | 30-40 | 60-80 | 1959-1965 |
| 1598 | Large Barrel (Port or Whisky) | 5 | 30-40 | 60-80 | 1959-1965 |
| 1615 | Babycham Fawn | 4 | 40-50 | 80-100 | 1959-1974 |
| 1625 | Woodbine ash tray | — | 20-25 | 40-50 | 1959-1960 |
| 1672 | Double Diamond face jug | 6½ | 150-200 | 300-400 | 1960-1961 |
| 1679 | Double Diamond Public House Plaque | 8¾ x 10 wide | 150-200 | 300-400 | 1960-1965 |
| 1680 | Double Diamond man Plaque | 5¼ x 5¼ | 100-125 | 200-250 | 1960-1965 |

| Model No | Name of Model | Height inches | Current Value £ | US$ | Production Period |
|---|---|---|---|---|---|
| 1681 | Double Diamond dog Plaque | $4\frac{3}{4}$ L x $1\frac{3}{4}$ | 80-100 | 160-200 | 1960-1965 |
| 1741/1 | Lord Mayor water jug (red bottle top) | $8\frac{1}{2}$ | 50-75 | 100-150 | 1961-1967 |
| 1741/2 | Lord Mayor water jug (green bottle top) | $8\frac{1}{2}$ | 50-75 | 100-150 | 1986-1987 |
| 1820 | Barrel B | $2\frac{1}{8}$ | 10-15 | 20-30 | 1962-1986 |
| 1821 | Carrera's 'Guardsman' Cigarettes Tankard | $5\frac{1}{4}$ | 40-50 | 80-100 | 1962-1965 |
| 1829 | Catto's Sportsman figure and dog | $11\frac{1}{2}$ | 200-250 | 400-500 | 1962-1965 |
| 1850 | Double Diamond lamp | $6\frac{1}{8}$ | 30-40 | 60-80 | 1962-1965 |
| 1856 | Double Diamond dish | — | 20-30 | 40-60 | 1962-1965 |
| 1869 | Dubonnet stand | $7\frac{1}{2}$ x $4\frac{1}{4}$ | 20-25 | 40-50 | 1963-1967 |
| 1870 | Dubonnet bottle | $5\frac{1}{2}$ | 20-25 | 40-50 | 1963-1967 |
| 1871 | Dubonnet poodle | $4\frac{1}{8}$ | 60-80 | 120-160 | 1963-1967 |
| 1872 | Dubonnet bulldog | $3\frac{3}{4}$ | 60-80 | 120-160 | 1963-1967 |
| 1946 | Timpsons the shoemaker dish | $3\frac{1}{2}$ | 40-60 | 80-120 | 1964-1966 |
| 1955 | Smiths Crisps Plaque | $7\frac{1}{4}$ x 2 | 40-60 | 80-120 | 1964-1965 |
| 1983 | Canada Dry ash tray | 9 | 20-30 | 40-60 | 1964-1967 |
| 1984 | Rothmans lamp | $4\frac{1}{2}$ | 30-40 | 60-80 | 1964-1967 |
| 1990 | Dulux dog | $12\frac{1}{2}$ | 250-300 | 500-600 | 1964-1970 |
| 1999 | Bath oil bottle & stopper for Cussons | $7\frac{1}{2}$ | 10-20 | 20-40 | 1966-1967 |
| 2000 | Covered bath salt jar for Cussons | $5\frac{1}{4}$ | 10-20 | 20-40 | 1966-1967 |
| 2001 | Bourne & Hollingsworth ash tray | 8 x $6\frac{1}{2}$ | 20-25 | 40-50 | 1964-1967 |
| 2009 | Skol lamp | 6 | 30-40 | 60-80 | 1965-1968 |
| 2010 | Double Diamond lamp | $5\frac{1}{2}$ | 30-40 | 60-80 | 1965-1968 |
| 2011 | Skol lamp | 6 | 30-40 | 60-80 | 1965-1968 |
| 2018 | Double Diamond lamp | $5\frac{1}{2}$ | 30-40 | 60-80 | 1965-1968 |
| 2033 | Fishermans flask B | $3\frac{3}{4}$ | 10-15 | 20-30 | 1965-1970 |
| 2047 | Gallagher ash bowl | 9x 7 | 20-30 | 40-60 | 1965-1968 |
| 2048 | Les Leston steering wheel ash bowl | 7 $\frac{1}{4}$ | 30-40 | 60-80 | 1965-1967 |
| *2051 | Nessie (Loch Ness Monster) B, 2 models: one with head stopper one with base stopper | 3 | 10-15 | 20-30 | 1965-1986 |
| 2052 | Piccadilly ash tray | $8\frac{1}{8}$ | 20-30 | 40-60 | 1965-1970 |
| 2053 | Gallagher water jug | $5\frac{3}{8}$ | 30-40 | 60-80 | 1965-1970 |
| 2055 | Craven A oval ash tray | 11 x $6\frac{5}{8}$ | 20-30 | 40-60 | 1966-1970 |
| 2056 | Pheasant flask B | $3\frac{1}{2}$ | 10-15 | 20-30 | 1966-1970 |
| 2057 | Pike flask B | $3\frac{1}{2}$ | 10-15 | 20-30 | 1966-1970 |
| 2058 | Deer flask B | $3\frac{1}{2}$ | 10-15 | 20-30 | 1966-1970 |
| 2060 | Hunts (lady rider on horse jumping fence) Plaque | $7\frac{3}{8}$ | 200-300 | 400-600 | 1966-1970 |
| 2076 | Robert Burns cottage flask B | $3\frac{1}{2}$ | 10-15 | 20-30 | 1966-1971 |
| 2077 | Edinburgh Castle flask B | $3\frac{1}{2}$ | 10-15 | 20-30 | 1966-1970 |
| 2079 | Watneys Plaque | $6\frac{1}{4}$ | 40-50 | 80-100 | 1966-1970 |
| 2086 | Beswick Plaque (Black & Gold) | $2\frac{1}{2}$ | 40-50 | 80-100 | 1966-1980 |
| 2088 | Peters Griffin Woodward bust USA dept. store | $3\frac{1}{2}$ | 50-75 | 100-150 | 1967-1970 |
| 2092 | Peters Griffin Woodward character jug USA dept. store | 5 | 75-100 | 150-200 | 1967-1970 |
| *2104 | Eagle flask B | $4\frac{3}{8}$ | 10-15 | 20-30 | 1967-1986 |
| 2115 | Pall Mall ash tray | $9\frac{3}{4}$ x $4\frac{3}{4}$ | 20-30 | 40-60 | 1967-1969 |
| 2180 | Tower Bridge flask | $3\frac{1}{2}$ | 10-15 | 20-30 | 1968-1971 |

117

| Model No | Name of Model | Height inches | Current Value £ | US$ | Production Period |
|---|---|---|---|---|---|
| 2185 | Arundel Castle flask | 4½ | 10-15 | 20-30 | 1968-1971 |
| 2192 | Benson & Hedges square ash tray | 5 | 20-30 | 40-60 | 1968-1975 |
| 2206 | Deer flask | 3½ | 10-15 | 20-30 | 1968-1971 |
| 2207 | Trout flask | 3½ | 10-15 | 20-30 | 1968-1971 |
| 2208 | Pheasant flask | 3½ | 10-15 | 20-30 | 1968-1971 |
| 2218 | Benson & Hedges orb ash tray | 7 Dia· | 20-30 | 40-60 | 1968-1975 |
| 2219 | Craven A ash tray | 8 Dia | 20-30 | 40-60 | 1968-1970 |
| 2237 | Babycham concave Plaque | 6¼ x 3⅜ | 50-75 | 100-150 | 1968-1970 |
| 2241 | Hamlet ash tray | 7½ x 5 | 20-30 | 40-60 | 1968-1975 |
| 2260 | Bemax jar & lid | — | 25-30 | 50-60 | 1969-1970 |
| 2261 | Hamlet cigars ash tray | 6⅛ x 6 | 20-30 | 40-60 | 1969-1975 |
| 2280 | Chante Clair cockerel jug | 9¾ | 200-250 | 400-500 | 1969-1971 |
| 2281 | Golden Eagle flask B | 10⅞ | 50-75 | 100-150 | 1969-1984 |
| 2318 | Golf Ball flask B | 1⅝ Dia | 10-15 | 20-30 | 1970-1986 |
| 2349 | Robert Burns flask B (bust) | — | 50-75 | 100-175 | 1971-1972 |
| **2350 | Haggis flask B | 2½ | 10-15 | 20-30 | 1971-1986 |
| 2486 | Bass Charrington (young couple behind letter E) | 9 | 100-125 | 200-250 | 1973-1976 |
| 2487 | Bass Charrington (rugby players behind letter E) | 9 | 100-125 | 200-250 | 1973-1976 |
| 2488 | Bass Charrington (squire & friend behind letter E) | 9 | 100-125 | 200-250 | 1973-1976 |
| 2506 | Bass Charington (Minton ewer jug) | 6¾ | 40-60 | 80-120 | 1974-1976 |
| 2514 | White Horse whisky (horse) | 6¾ | 400-500 | 800-1000 | 1974-1976 |
| ***2518 | Worthington (butcher & baker behind letter E) | 9 | 125-150 | 250-300 | 1974-1975 |
| ***2519 | Worthington (woman & dog behind letter E) | 9 | 125-150 | 250-300 | 1974-1975 |
| ***2520 | Worthington (parson & policeman behind letter E) | 9 | 125-150 | 250-300 | 1974-1975 |
| 2561 | Grouse for Mathew Gloag Ltd | 9⅜ | 80-100 | 160-200 | 1976-1984 |
| *2583 | Osprey flask B | 7¾ | 50-75 | 100-150 | 1977-1986 |
| **2636 | Squirrel flask B | 3½ | 20-25 | 40-50 | 1978-1986 |
| *2639 | Kestrel flask B | 6½ | 75-100 | 150-200 | 1979-1986 |
| *2640 | Buzzard flask B | 6½ | 75-100 | 150-200 | 1979-1986 |
| *2641 | Merlin flask B | 6½ | 75-100 | 150-200 | 1979-1986 |
| *2642 | Peregrine flask B | 6½ | 75-100 | 150-200 - | 1979-1986 |
| 2670 | Bunratty castle (5000 edition) | 6 | 30-40 | 60-80 | 1980-1983 |
| *2678 | Golden Eagle flask B | 10½ | 50-75 | 100-150 | 1984-1987 |
| **2686 | Otter flask B | 2¼ | 20-25 | 40-50 | 1981-1986 |
| **2687 | Badger flask B | 3 | 20-25 | 40-50 | 1981-1986 |
| **2693 | Seal flask B | 3⅞ | 20-25 | 40-50 | 1981-1986 |
| *2781 | Tawny Owl flask B | 6¼ | 75-100 | 150-200 | 1986-1987 |
| *2809 | Barn Owl flask B | 6¾ | 75-100 | 150-200 | 1986-1987 |
| *2825 | Short Eared Owl flask B | 6½ | 75-100 | 150-200 | 1986-1987 |
| 2826/1 | Snowy Owl flask B | 6 | 75-100 | 150-200 | 1986 only |
| *2826/2 | Snowy Owl flask W&M | 6½ | 75-100 | 150-200 | 1986-1987 |

B = Beneagles whisky container for Peter Thomson (Perth) Ltd.

*Re-introduced 1987 for Whyte & Mackay(Glasgow), now current and carrying the Royal Doulton backstamp

** Re-introduced 1987-1991 for Whyte & Mackay

***Limited production

# Christmas Around the World

(All carry the Beswick mark)

There are a growing number of collectors who seem to enjoy Christmas all year long by tracking down pieces with colourful, seasonal imagery. The fashion for collecting plates with a Christmas theme developed in the USA and it was originally for an American audience that Beswick introduced a series of annual plates depicting 'Christmas Around the World'. In order to convey the distinctive traditions of festivities in other lands, several different artists were invited to contribute to this collection and their artwork was then modelled in low relief by Beswick artists. Harry Sales, the company's design manager, visualised the first, 'Old England' in 1972. Chavela Castrejon was commissioned to design 'Christmas in Mexico' issued in 1973 and Dimitri Yordanov was responsible for 'Christmas in Bulgaria' for the 1974 plate. The remaining four plates were all designed by Alton Toby, his final scene of 'Christmas in America' completing the set of seven in 1978.

In addition to these plates, the Beswick artists experimented with a few relief modelled rectangular plaques portraying yuletide scenes in Dickensian mood but it would appear these did not go into production in any great quantity.

## Plates & Plaques

| Model No | Description | Size inches | Current Value £ | US$ | Plate or Plaque | Issue Date |
|---|---|---|---|---|---|---|
| 2376 | Christmas 1972 | 11¼ x 5½ | 150-200 | 300-400 | Plaque | 1972 |
| 2393 | Christmas in England | 8 x 8 | 25-35 | 50-70 | Plate | 1972 |
| 2419 | Christmas in Mexico | 8 x 8 | 25-35 | 50-70 | Plate | 1973 |
| 2430 | Christmas 1973 | 11¼ x 5½ | 150-200 | 300-400 | Plaque | 1973 |
| 2443 | Regent Street | 11 x 7 | 125-150 | 250-300 | Plaque | 1973 |
| 2444 | Christmas Ornament | | 75-100 | 150-200 | Plaque | 1973 |
| 2462 | Christmas in Bulgaria | 8 x 8 | 25-35 | 50-70 | Plate | 1974 |
| 2522 | Christmas in Norway | 8 x 8 | 25-35 | 50-70 | Plate | 1975 |
| 2538 | Christmas in Holland | 8 x 8 | 25-35 | 50-70 | Plate | 1976 |
| 2567 | Christmas in Poland | 8 x 8 | 25-35 | 50-70 | Plate | 1977 |
| 2598 | Christmas in America | 8 x 8 | 25-35 | 50-70 | Plate | 1978 |

# Christmas Carol Tankards

(All carry the Beswick Mark)

Dickens also provided the inspiration for the limited edition collection of tankards launched in 1971. Each year a scene from his classic *A Christmas Carol* was vividly modelled in low relief and admirably captured the spirit of the traditional English yuletide. The set of twelve was completed in 1982 and although the edition size was published as 15,000 each year, it is believed that the final number produced was less than this, with most going to the United States, Canada and Australia. However, the British collector can still find them at antique fairs and markets.

| Model No | Description | Value £ | US$ | Issue Date |
|---|---|---|---|---|
| 2351 | Cratchit & Scrooge | 40-50 | 80-100 | 1971 |
| 2375 | Carolers | 40-50 | 80-100 | 1972 |
| 2423 | Solicitation | 40-50 | 80-100 | 1973 |
| 2445 | Marley's Ghost | 30-40 | 60-80 | 1974 |
| 2523 | Ghost of Christmas Past | 30-40 | 60-80 | 1975 |
| 2539 | Ghost of Christmas Present | 30-40 | 60-80 | 1976 |
| 2568 | Ghost of Christmas Present | 30-40 | 60-80 | 1977 |
| 2599 | Ghost of Christmas Present | 30-40 | 60-80 | 1978 |
| 2624 | Ghost of Christmas Future | 30-40 | 60-80 | 1979 |
| 2657 | Scrooge Visits His Own Grave | 30-40 | 60-80 | 1980 |
| 2692 | Scrooge Going to Church | 30-40 | 60-80 | 1981 |
| 2764 | Christmas at Bob Cratchit's | 40-50 | 80-100 | 1982 |

*The final annual Christmas Tankard in the series of 12 was 1982 and this is the hardest to find*

# Commemoratives

(All carry the Beswick mark)

Royal Commemoratives produced by Beswick form a small but interesting collection. Like other pottery companies, Beswick issued pieces to commemorate the coronation of HRH Edward VIII but when he suddenly abdicated on December 10 1936, new wares featuring HRH George VI had to be prepared.

As well as two mugs, of which one was musical, Beswick obtained the reproduction rights for a collection of souvenirs modelled by Felix Weiss. These unusual commemoratives all depicted the bust of George VI and are listed below.

The next Royal coronation was that of HRH Elizabeth II in 1953 and the selection of mugs and trays issued for this occasion are also detailed below.

| Model No | Name of Model | Current Value £ | US$ | Production Period |
|---|---|---|---|---|
| 377 | Edward VIII Plaque | 60-80 | 120-160 | 1936-1937 |
| 445 | Edward VIII Coronation tankard | 30-40 | 60-80 | 1936-1937 |
| 446 | Edward VIII Coronation mug | 15-20 | 30-40 | 1936-1937 |
| 451 | Edward VIII bust | 60-80 | 120-160 | 1936-1937 |
| 458 | Edward VIII covered jar | 60-80 | 120-160 | 1936-1937 |
| 461 | George VI Coronation musical mug | 75-100 | 150-200 | 1937-1938 |
| 462 | George VI Coronation mug | 15-20 | 30-40 | 1937-1938 |
| 468 | George VI bust | 60-80 | 120-160 | 1937-1938 |
| 469 | George VI bust | 50-60 | 100-120 | 1937-1938 |
| 470 | George VI plaque | 60-80 | 120-160 | 1937-1938 |
| 471 | George VI plaque | 50-60 | 100-120 | 1937-1938 |
| 472 | George VI bookend | 50-60 | 100-120 | 1937-1938 |
| 1250 | Elizabeth II Coronation mug | 15-20 | 30-40 | 1952-1954 |
| 1251 | Elizabeth II Coronation beaker | 15-20 | 30-40 | 1952-1954 |
| 1252 | Elizabeth II Embossed Coronation mug | 20-25 | 40-50 | 1952-1954 |
| 1253 | Elizabeth II Coronation tray (large) | 20-25 | 40-50 | 1952-1954 |
| 1254 | Elizabeth II Coronation tray (small) | 15-20 | 30-40 | 1952-1954 |

# Shakespeare Series Ware

(All carry the Beswick mark)

The plays of William Shakespeare (1564-1616) have been a fertile source of inspiration for Beswick artists. Mr Hallam, Mr Gredington and Mr Orwell have interpreted some of the most famous scenes in a series of jugs, tankards and mugs, superbly modelled in low relief. *Romeo and Juliet*, Shakespeare's first tragedy and perhaps his best known work, is represented by a jug and a wall plaque both depicting the fond farewell. The other plaque in the series features characters from the famous comedy *As You Like It* and the quotation "That would I, were I of all kingdoms king". Suitable inscriptions appear on all the Shakespeare wares. Hamlet's famous soliloquy "To be or not to be" is inscribed on a tankard depicting a scene from the play and a jug features the Prince of Denmark with his father's ghost and the quotation "Hamlet — be thou a spirit of health?" Sir John Falstaff, Shakespeare's jovial knight also features on both a jug and a tankard. He was so popular with audiences in the sixteenth century that he appears in *Henry IV* Part I, *Henry V* and later in *The Merry Wives of Windsor*.

All these Shakespearean wares are not difficult to find today, but the last two, depicting scenes from *A Midsummer Night's Dream*, which were added to the set in 1955, can be quite elusive.

| Model No | Name of Model | Height inches | Current Value £ | US$ | Production Period |
|---|---|---|---|---|---|
| 1126 | Falstaff jug | 8 | 80-100 | 160-200 | 1948-1973 |
| 1127 | Falstaff tankard | 4 | 25-30 | 50-80 | 1948-1973 |
| 1146 | Hamlet jug | 8¼ | 80-100 | 160-200 | 1949-1973 |
| 1147 | Hamlet tankard | 4¼ | 25-30 | 50-60 | 1949-1973 |
| 1209 | As You Like It wall plaque | 12 dia | 80-100 | 160-200 | 1950-1969 |
| 1210 | Romeo & Juliet wall plaque | 12 dia | 80-100 | 160-200 | 1951-1969 |
| 1214 | Juliet jug | 8¼ | 80-100 | 160-200 | 1951-1973 |
| 1215 | Juliet mug | 4 | 25-30 | 50-60 | 1951-1973 |
| 1366 | A Midsummer Night's Dream – jug | 8 | 80-100 | 160-200 | 1955-1973 |
| 1368 | A Midsummer Night's Dream – mug | 4¼ | 40-60 | 80-120 | 1955-1973 |
| *2213 | Bust of Shakespeare | 3 | 30-50 | 60-100 | 1968-1970 |
| *2243 | Bust of Shakespeare on pedestal | 5 | 40-60 | 80-120 | 1968-1970 |

*Can be found decorated or plain white, with white being priced lower.*

# Trentham Art Wares

During the 1930s a seven year agreement was made between Beswick and Hardy, a wholesaler based in Nottingham, for items to be designed and produced at Beswick, but to be marketed under the name of 'Trentham Art Wares'.

Approximately two hundred different items were produced and marked with the Beswick model number and 'Made in England' impressed on the base together with the 'Trentham Art Wares' backstamp. Most pieces were vases or jugs but there were approximately thirty animals, figures or birds and it is likely that these only carried the backstamp.

The agreement lapsed in 1941 and Beswick were then free to continue production of the more popular items, but carrying only their own backstamp or impressed mark.

Several of these pieces continued in production until the mid sixties and the following list gives all known model numbers which were subject to this agreement.

*Model Numbers*

| | | | |
|---|---|---|---|
| 21-48 | 380/84/85 | 653-657 | 902-914 |
| 76/77 | 422/24/28 | 668 | 918-922 |
| 79-81 | 431/32/34/35 | 675-680 | 955-959 |
| 91/94/95/98 | 439/40 | 688 | 987 |
| 129-132 | 444 | 693/94/99 | |
| 136 | 447-449 | 700/02 | |
| 140 | 490/92/94/95/96 | 731 | |
| 148-167 | 498-500 | 760-62/65 | |
| 289-292 | 503-505 | 770-784 | |
| 299-301 | 546-548 | 800-809 | |
| 306/07 | 550/52/54/55 | 813/15/19 | |
| 345-357 | 558/60/62/63 | 827/29 | |
| 362-367 | 566/68-70 | 836/38 | |
| 373/79 | 573 | | |

*Standard Trentham backstamp with impressed shape number.*

# Britannia Collection

(All backstamped Beswick)

This range of ceramic studies is taken from the existing Beswick collection, with the exception of the Special Commission Unicorn, and is finished in a rich bronze glaze with subtle shading. This new decorative process was developed by Graham Tongue, Design Manager at the John Beswick Studio in 1989.

| Model No | Name of Model | Height inches | Value £ | US$ | Production Period |
|---|---|---|---|---|---|
| 868 | Huntsman | 10 | 80-100 | 160-200 | 1989-1992 |
| *981 | Stag (small) | 9 | 30-40 | 60-80 | 1989-1992 |
| 1018 | Bald Eagle | 7¼ | 30-40 | 60-80 | 1989-1992 |
| *2542 | Hereford Bull | 7½ | 80-100 | 160-200 | 1989-1992 |
| *2549 | Polled Hereford Bull | 6¼ | 80-100 | 160-200 | 1989-1992 |
| 2629 | Stag (large) | 13½ | 100-125 | 200-250 | 1989-1992 |
| *2688 | Spirit of the Wind (horse) | 9 | 50-60 | 100-120 | 1989-1992 |
| 2760 | Pheasant | 10½ | 100-125 | 200-250 | 1989-1992 |
| *2914 | Spirit of Earth (shire horse) | 8½ | 50-60 | 100-120 | 1989-1992 |
| *2986 | Setter | 8½ | 30-40 | 60-80 | 1989-1992 |
| *3011 | Pointer | 8⅜ | 30-40 | 60-80 | 1989-1992 |
| *3021 | Unicorn | 9 | 60-80 | 120-160 | 1989-1992 |
| *3066 | Retriever | 7½ | 30-40 | 60-80 | 1989-1992 |

*on ceramic base

# Catalogue Specials

Since 1987 a number of current items have been mounted on ceramic bases, for direct purchase from mail order catalogues.

Most had a polished brass name-plate affixed to the base, with a suitably descriptive title. Now discontinued, they are an unusual addition to the Beswick collection, but do tend to take up a lot of space.

In addition, there was at least one example of a Shire horse (2914) being mounted on a ceramic base with a green top instead of the production 'earth' colour. This order was for an American TV station and all were sold in this way. The backstamp was circular and read 'Beswick — Made in England'.

Other combinations can also be found.

| Model No | Name-plate Title | Model names |
|---|---|---|
| 1558/1678 | 'Watch It' | Siamese Cat/Mouse |
| 2950/1436 | 'Good Friends' | Playful puppy 'Nap Time'/Kitten |
| 1460/1436 | 'Sharing' | Dachshund sitting/Kitten |
| 818/1034 | 'Horses Great & Small' | Shire/Shetland Foal |
| 2267/2110 | 'Jenny's Baby' | Donkey/Donkey Foal |
| 1765/1828 | 'Ewe and I' | Sheep |
| 999/1000 | — | Doe and Fawn |

| Model No | Name-plate Title | Model names |
|---|---|---|
| 1452/1453 | — | Pigs |
| 1362/1249 | — | Cow and Calf — black |
| 1362/1249 | — | Cow and Calf — brown |
| 1886/3093 | 'Playtime' | Kitten/Ball of Wool |
| 1501/2262/63 | 'Tally Ho!' | Huntsman and 2 Hounds |
| 2689/2536 | — | Black Beauty and Foal (in gloss) |
| 1436/1678/DA222 | 'Solid Friendship | Cat/mouse/bulldog |
| 3464 | Made up of rearing horse 868 and three hounds 2262-64 on a modelled base which is set on wood base 14 inches long. Available 1995 only. | |

# Models mounted on a wood plinth

New introductions for 1994 included the following current models mounted on a wooden base with a brass plaque. All are gloss finish and all are now withdrawn.

| Model No. | Model name | Current Value £ | US$ | Production Period |
|---|---|---|---|---|
| 3075/1827 | Charolais Cow and Calf | 50-60 | 100-120 | 1993-1996 |
| 1362/1249 | Freisan Cow and Calf | 50-60 | 100-120 | 1993-1996 |
| 1360/1827 | Hereford Cow and Calf | 50-60 | 100-120 | 1993-1996 |
| 1345/1249 | Jersey Cow and Calf | 50-60 | 100-120 | 1993-1996 |
| 1765/1828 | Black Faced Sheep and Lamb | 25-30 | 50-60 | 1993-1996 |
| 1452 | Sow — Large White | 20-25 | 40-50 | 1993-1995 |
| 1453 | Boar — Large White | 20-25 | 40-50 | 1993-1995 |
| 1016 | Standing Fox | 30-40 | 60-100 | 1993-1996 |
| 999/1000 | Doe and Fawn | 30-40 | 60-100 | 1993-1996 |

# Table models

(All backstamped Beswick)

| Model No. | Model name | Size | Current Value £ | US$ | Production Period |
|---|---|---|---|---|---|
| 1610 | Firefly dinghy | 5½ | 50-75 | 100-150 | 1960-1962 |
| 1633 | GP 14 yacht | 11 | 75-100 | 150-200 | 1960-1962 |
| 1634 | Heron yacht | 8¼ | 100-125 | 200-250 | 1960-1962 |

# Backstamps

The dating of backstamps holds a great deal of interest for all collectors and the task has not been made easy by the fairly wide variety used by Beswick. In addition, several designs of adhesive labels have been used since the late 1950s up until 1989, when the practice ceased. In the late 1960s, horses and cattle had their name printed on a label, which was tied around the neck. This practice ceased about 1972. Round about 1987 the tie-on label method was revived on most items produced at that time, but this was a standard green John Beswick type and did not apply specifically to that model. These are still in use today. Other specially designed tie-on labels have recently been used on the Little Loveables, English Country Friend and Pig Prom series.

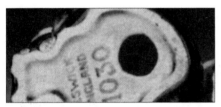

*Left: impressed name and number. Base large enough to accommodate both. In use 1938-1972. Right: Impressed number only on smaller base. Backstamped name. In use 1938-72*

*Thunderbirds special stamp. In use 1992 only.*

*Transfer backstamp in use 1985-1990*

*Extensively used on ornamental ware in the 1950s and 1960s.*

*Left: Special edition, by Peter Rabbit & Friends, with two gold buttons and gold backstamp.*

*This is an impressed mark and was in use from about 1954 until 1971.*

*The numbered limited edition of 1997 pieces of Mrs Rabbit and the Four Bunnies.*

Beswick Ware
MADE IN ENGLAND
BEATRIX POTTER'S
JEMIMA PUDDLE-DUCK
BESWICK CENTENARY
1894 – 1994
© F. WARNE & CO. 1993
© 1993 ROYAL DOULTON

*The special centenary backstamp for Peter Rabbit – large size – in 1994*

*A typical early gold backstamp.*

*A gold backstamp, part handwritten.*

*Early gold backstamp with round "Beswick England".*

*Hummel backstamp, fully detailed.*

CHOO-CHOO ™
© 1996 H-B PROD., INC.
LICENSED BY CPL
© 1996 ROYAL DOULTON
EXCLUSIVE EDITION OF 2,000
FOR THE DOULTON &
BESWICK FAIRS IN ENGLAND

*Doulton and Beswick Fairs in England backstamp.*

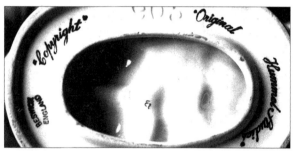

*Unusual style for the three Anglund models*

*English Country Friends.*

*Another backstamp in gold.*

*UKI Ceramics backstamp.*

127

*Kingfisher 2579 – not put into production.*

# AFTER "WARLORD" WHAT NEXT?

If you purchased the Special Commission Dartmoor Pony in 1996, then you may be interested in his mare "Another Bunch", to be released in the Autumn of 1997.

This is a completely new model and will again only be available from

**Doug Middleweek**
**The Old Glebe House and The Smithy**
**Widecombe-in-the-Moor**
**Newton Abbot**
**Devon TQ13 7TB**
**Tel: 01364 621226**

*or from*

**Harvey May (Beswick author)**
**Tel: 01702 549275**

*A brand new lying foal will be available in 1998. All will carry the "Beswick' backstamp and be limited to 1,500 pieces each.*

# THE COLLECTOR

**CENTRAL LONDON EXCITING MEETING PLACE FOR BESWICK COLLECTORS**

*Situated next to Alfies — The UK's Largest Antique Market*

Royal Doulton and Beswick Specialist

— also in stock —

Contemporary figurines and collectables by Lladro, Wade,
Royal Worcester, Lilliput Lane, Moorcroft, Copenhagen, Goebel,
Spode, Coalport, Bossons, David Winter, Pendelfin, etc

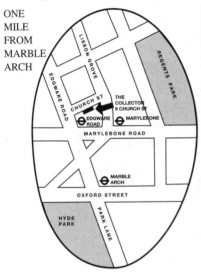

ONE MILE FROM MARBLE ARCH

## The Collector Shop
### *RUN by Collectors*
### *FOR Collectors*

OPEN SEVEN DAYS
9.30am — 5.30 pm
Sunday 10am — 2pm

*50 PAGE ILLUSTRATED CATALOGUE*
*AVAILABLE ON SUBSCRIPTION*

Tel: 0171 706 4586/Fax: 0171 706 2948
*From the USA or Canada call Toll Free*
*1-800 514 8176 x2212*
*e-mail: collector@globalnet.co.uk*

## The Collector
**9 Church Street, Marylebone, London NW8 8DT**

 **WORLDWIDE MAIL ORDER SERVICE** **VISA**

# Beswick Sales
# at Phillips

*Phillips hold two Doulton, Wade and Beswick sales a year
(usually May and October).
We are always delighted to offer free advice regarding
Beswick by telephone (0171 468 8233) or to
welcome you to our Beswick auctions.
Closing date for entries is approx 8 weeks prior to sale.
For more information, please call Mark Oliver
on the number quoted.*

Phillips
101 New Bond Street
London W1Y 0AS
Telephone: 0171 629 6602

 Collectors
Club

**Notice to all collectors**

The *Beswick Collectors Club* has been formed to foster interest in Beswick ware, both old and new, to encourage collectors and people with an interest in Beswick to be able to meet or communicate with other members.

Meetings are held periodically around the country to give members an opportunity to socialise, buy, sell, or exchange Beswick pieces.

**To join, intending Members must first subscribe to *Collecting Doulton* magazine which is the main means of communication within the Club.**

Funding for the *Beswick Collectors Club* (postal charges, paper, printing, telephone calls etc) comes from an allowance in the charge for attending meetings and is in no way connected with the subscription to the *Collecting Doulton* magazine.

*For any further information please contact:*

| | | |
|---|---|---|
| Alan Ruddle (co-ordinator) | Derbyshire | 01773 822941 |
| Tony Strawford | Staffs | 01922 56235 |
| Marilyn Sweet | Lancs | 01204 695793 |

or by contacting

*Collecting Doulton & Beswick* magazine     0181 318 9580

or writing to

Francis Joseph Publications
15 St Swithuns Road, London SE13 6RQ

# Collecting Doulton
# & Collecting Beswick

Over the past two years *Collecting Doulton* incorporating *Collecting Beswick* has gone from strength to strength. We are independent publishers who cater solely for the collector. We give objective news and views. We offer limited introductions that are not obtainable anywhere else, and we have contributions from the best experts around – Jocelyn Lukins, Doug Pinchin, Louise Irvine, Harvey May. There are always interesting features, new introductions, lists of the latest deletions, collectors buy and sell. Why not join us today?

**Beswick Collectors** – please note that by subscribing to our magazine you will automatically become a member of the Beswick Collectors Club. This will give you regular updates on events in your area and will entitle you to purchase the exclusive limited edition Beswick collectors piece for that year.

*Special BCC edition of Dun colour Mare and Foal only available to members*

NOTES